PERGAMON INTERNATIONAL LIBRARY
of Science, Technology, Engineering and Social Studies
*The 1000-volume original paperback library in aid of education,
industrial training and the enjoyment of leisure*

Publisher: Robert Maxwell, M.C.

ELECTRONICS—
from Theory into Practice

THE PERGAMON TEXTBOOK
INSPECTION COPY SERVICE

An inspection copy of any book published in the Pergamon International Library will gladly
be sent to academic staff without obligation for their consideration for course adoption or
recommendation. Copies may be retained for a period of 60 days from receipt and returned if
not suitable. When a particular title is adopted or recommended for adoption for class use
and the recommendation results in a sale of 12 or more copies, the inspection copy may be
retained with our compliments. If after examination the lecturer decides that the book is not
suitable for adoption but would like to retain it for his personal library, then a discount of 10%
is allowed on the invoiced price. The Publishers will be pleased to receive suggestions for
revised editions and new titles to be published in this important International Library.

APPLIED ELECTRICITY AND ELECTRONICS DIVISION

General Editor: P. HAMMOND

Contents of Volume 2

v

Contents of Volume 1

Preface to Volume 2

In Volume 1 the reader is introduced to electronic devices and is shown how data sheets, provided by the manufacturer, are used in design calculations. Two chapters are devoted to the subject of amplifiers, both tuned and untuned, each containing a brief treatment of theory limited to the extraction of necessary design relationships. Design procedures are established, followed by worked design examples to meet given specifications.

Volume 2 contains five chapters devoted to other specific topics which are treated in a similar manner. Thus, Chapter 6, on negative feedback amplifiers, includes a wide range of worked examples to illustrate the use of the ubiquitous operational amplifier. There follows chapters on power supplies, sinusoidal oscillators and waveform generators, and the final design chapter is concerned with digital techniques. The main text is concluded with a chapter on general electronic engineering practice. This includes a survey of resistor and capacitor types, screening, earths and earth loops, and some guidance on the practical use of TTL devices.

Since the publication of the first edition of this book there have been dramatic advances in electronic technology, so that the thermionic valve has, except in highly specialized applications, been eliminated. Nevertheless, the authors feel that some place should be retained in the literature for these devices, if only for reference purposes. Accordingly, an appendix is devoted to this topic in this completely revised edition.

Cranfield   J. E. FISHER

Design Examples

CHAPTER 6

Negative Feedback Amplifiers

6.1. Introduction

By feeding back a portion of the output to the input, the performance of an amplifier can be significantly changed. Figure 6.1 represents the flow of information in a feedback network, and A can be either a voltage or a current amplifier.

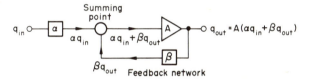

Fig. 6.1. A basic feedback structure. The input and output quantities can be either voltages or currents depending on the form of amplifier A. α and β are fractions of the input and output quantities present at the summing point.

Gain of feedback amplifier
As shown in Fig. 6.1, the output quantity

$$q_{out} = A(\alpha q_{in} + \beta q_{out}), \qquad (6.1)$$

or

$$q_{out} = \frac{\alpha A}{1 - A\beta} q_{in}. \qquad (6.2)$$

In most examples α and β will be made up of passive elements and have values of unity or less. The amplifier gain A will generally be much greater than unity.

211

Loop gain

The product $A\beta$ is the loop gain. It is usually much greater than unity and has a negative sign if the feedback is to be negative. Either A or β can be negative. If A is negative the feedback amplifier will provide signal inversion.

For $A\beta \gg 1$,

$$q_{out} \doteq \frac{-\alpha}{\beta} q_{in} \quad \text{[from eqn. (6.2)].} \tag{6.3}$$

Example. If $\alpha = 1$, $\beta = 0.2$ and $A = -50$, the loop gain is $A\beta = -10$, and

$$q_{out} = \frac{-50}{1+10} q_{in} \quad \text{[from eqn. (6.2)]}$$

$$= -4.5 \, q_{in}.$$

If the approximation of eqn. (6.3) is used,

$$q_{out} \doteq -\frac{1}{0.2} q_{in} = -5 q_{in}.$$

If there is no signal inversion in the amplifier, that is $A = 50$, β must be negative for negative feedback. Then,

$$q_{out} = \frac{50}{1+10} q_{in} \quad \text{[from eqn. (6.2)],}$$

and the output signal is of the same sign as the input signal.

Stabilization of gain

Equation (6.3) shows that if the loop gain is sufficiently large, the over-all gain is independent of the A gain. Let

$$\frac{q_{out}}{q_{in}} = G = \frac{\alpha A}{1 - A\beta},$$

then

$$\frac{dG}{dA} = \frac{(1-A\beta)+A\beta}{(1-A\beta)^2} \cdot \alpha = \frac{\alpha A}{1-A\beta} \cdot \frac{1}{1-A\beta} \cdot \frac{1}{A},$$

$$= \frac{G}{A(1-A\beta)}.$$

Thus

$$\frac{\Delta G}{G} = \frac{\Delta A}{A} \cdot \frac{1}{1 - A\beta}, \qquad (6.4)$$

where $(1 - A\beta) > 1$ for negative feedback, and $\Delta A/A$ and $\Delta G/G$ are fractional changes in A amplifier gain and feedback amplifier gain respectively.

The change in A gain is reduced by the term $1/(1 - A\beta)$ for the feedback amplifier. Since, in general, non-linear distortion arises from changes in gain with signal amplitude, such distortion is reduced by the same factor, when negative feedback is applied.

Extension of bandwidth
The expressions so far obtained show that changes in gain due to variations in frequency are reduced by the factor $1/(1 - A\beta)$. Thus the bandwidth of the A amplifier is extended by this factor, as $1 - A\beta$ is greater than unity for negative feedback.

6.2. Feedback connections

The basic feedback connections illustrated in Fig. 6.2 are the four feedback connections of network theory. The amplifiers and the feedback networks are connected as two-ports. The voltage amplifier of Fig. 6.2a has the two input ports joined in series and the

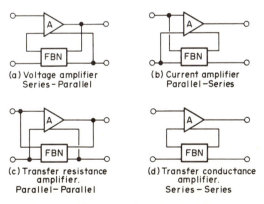

(a) Voltage amplifier
Series-Parallel

(b) Current amplifier
Parallel-Series

(c) Transfer resistance
amplifier.
Parallel-Parallel

(d) Transfer conductance
amplifier.
Series-Series

Fig. 6.2. Basic feedback amplifier connections. The amplifier has gain A, and FBN represents the feedback network.

input current to the amplifier also flows through the feedback network (FBN). (The current which enters the upper terminal of a two-port network must leave by its lower terminal.) The output ports are parallel connected, as in this case the output voltage is common to each port, and the output current is shared between

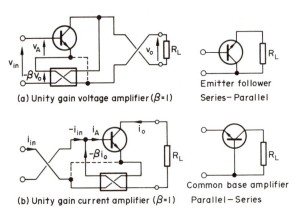

(a) Unity gain voltage amplifier ($\beta=1$)   Emitter follower
                                                 Series–Parallel

(b) Unity gain current amplifier ($\beta=1$)   Common base amplifier
                                                 Parallel–Series

Fig. 6.3. Two basic feedback systems which require no element apart from the amplifying device.

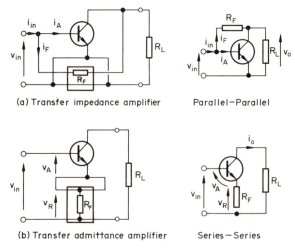

(a) Transfer impedance amplifier   Parallel–Parallel

(b) Transfer admittance amplifier   Series–Series

Fig. 6.4. Together with those of Fig. 6.3, these two systems represent the four feedback systems of network theory.

them. The current amplifier has the inputs paralleled, and the outputs are in series as in Fig. 6.2b. The other two connections are the remaining possible combinations.

The simplest realizations of the basic feedback connections are shown in Figs. 6.3 and 6.4. Those of Fig. 6.3 require no elements apart from the amplifying device, and represent unity feedback systems. In (a), all the output voltage is fed back in series with the input, while in (b) the whole output current is fed into the amplifier input. In each case, the feedback factor β is unity, and the connections form the *common emitter* (emitter follower) and *common base* configurations, obtained by applying negative feedback to the common emitter device. As the feedback factor is unity, the gain is unity in each case.

(a) *Voltage gain of the series–parallel connection*
In Fig. 6.3a,

$$v_{in} = v_A + v_o,$$

where v_A is the transistor input voltage, and $\beta = -1$. If the gain is high, $v_A \ll v_o$ and $v_{in} \doteq v_o$.

The system has unity gain, which is of course the case for the *emitter follower*. This is a transistor, operating in common emitter connection with unity series–parallel feedback, an arrangement which always limits the voltage gain to unity if the load resistance is not excessive. Such will be the case for all transistors, even though their actual common emitter voltage gains vary widely. The essential feature of negative feedback is that gain is dependent on some external property of the network, such as the cross-over network of Fig. 6.3a which provides negative feedback, and is almost entirely independent of the device parameters.

More generally, in Fig. 6.3a, if v_A is the A amplifier input voltage, and the fraction of output voltage fed back to the input is β,

$$v_{in} = v_A + \beta v_0 = \frac{v_0}{A} + \beta v_0$$

$$= \frac{v_0}{A}(1 + A\beta).$$

Thus,

$$\frac{v_0}{v_{in}} = \frac{A}{1 + A\beta} \doteqdot \frac{1}{\beta},$$ (6.5)

if the loop gain $A\beta \gg 1$.

Input resistance for series–parallel feedback

Because the output voltage is fed back in series with the amplifier input, as in Fig. 6.5a, the voltage across the input resistance, R_i, is reduced from v_{in} to

$$v_A = v_{in} - \beta v_o = v_{in} - A\beta v_A,$$

or

$$v_{in} = (1 + A\beta)v_A.$$

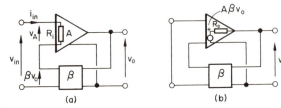

(a)   (b)

Fig. 6.5. Determination of (a) input resistance and (b) output resistance, for the series–parallel connection.

The input current is the current through R_i,

$$i_{in} = \frac{v_A}{R_i} = \frac{v_{in}}{(1 + A\beta)R_i},$$

or

$$R_{in} = \frac{v_{in}}{i_{in}} = (1 + A\beta)R_i.$$ (6.6)

The A amplifier input resistance is effectively increased by the loop gain of the feedback system. Since the voltage gain of a transistor in common emitter operation is approximately

$$A = -\frac{h_{fe}R_L}{h_{ie}},$$

from the exact expression in Table 1.2, the loop gain of the emitter follower is

$$A\beta \doteq \frac{h_{fe}}{h_{ie}}R_L.$$

Assuming that the input resistance to the transistor is h_{ie}, the emitter follower input resistance,

$$R_{in} = (1 + A\beta)R_i,$$
$$\doteq \frac{h_{fe}}{h_{ie}}R_L h_{ie},$$
$$\doteq h_{fe}R_L, \tag{6.7}$$

i.e. proportional to the load resistance.

Output resistance for series–parallel feedback

The output resistance is independent of the input signal. Let the input be zero as in Fig. 6.5b. The voltage across R_o is then

$$v_{Ao} = v_o - A\beta v_o,$$
$$= v_o(1 + A\beta) \quad \text{for negative feedback.}$$

The output current, neglecting the current supplied to the feedback network, is

$$i_o = \frac{v_{Ao}}{R_o} = \frac{v_o(1 + A\beta)}{R_o}.$$

Thus, the output resistance is

$$R_{out} = \frac{v_o}{i_o} = \frac{R_o}{1 + A\beta}, \tag{6.8}$$

i.e. the A amplifier output resistance is divided by the loop gain. For large loop gains the output resistance is low.

(b) *Parallel–series feedback current gain*

As in Fig. 6.3b, a proportion of the output current is fed back to the input.

$$i_{in} + \beta i_o = -i_A. \tag{6.9}$$

But,

$$i_o = A_i i_A, \quad \text{where } A_i \text{ is the current gain,}$$

so

$$i_{in} + \beta i_o = - i_o / A_i,$$

or,

$$\frac{i_o}{i_{in}} = \frac{- A_i}{1 + A_i \beta}.$$

Thus, for common base operation, current gain

$$\frac{i_o}{i_{in}} = \frac{- h_{fe}}{1 + h_{fe}}$$

if the load resistance is not excessive.

Input resistance for parallel–series feedback

$$R_{in} = \frac{v_{in}}{i_{in}} = \frac{v_{in}}{- i_A (1 + A_i \beta)}, \quad \text{from eqn. (6.9)}$$

$$= \frac{R_A}{1 + A_i \beta},$$

since the A amplifier input resistance equals $- v_{in}/i_A$. Thus,

$$R_{in} \doteq \frac{h_{ie}}{1 + h_{fe}}, \tag{6.10}$$

and approximately equals $1/y_{fe}$ for the common base connection, since $y_{fe} = h_{fe}/h_{ie}$.

Output resistance for parallel–series feedback (Fig. 6.6)

Consider the input current i_{in} to be zero. This does not modify the output resistance,

$$v_o = (i_o + A_i \beta i_o) R_o,$$

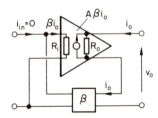

Fig. 6.6. Measurement of output resistance for parallel–series connection. The current i_o is injected and the resulting v_o measured.

or,

$$v_o/i_o = R_o(1 + A_i\beta). \qquad (6.11)$$

The output resistance of the A amplifier is enhanced by the negative feedback.

(c) *Parallel–parallel feedback*

The input current for the arrangement of Fig. 6.4a is

$$i_{in} = i_F + i_A \doteq i_F,$$

if the current gain is sufficiently large. The output voltage,

$$v_o \doteq - R_F i_F,$$

as v_{in} is small, whence

$$\frac{v_o}{i_{in}} = - R_F. \qquad (6.12)$$

Since it relates output voltage to input current, R_F is the *Transfer Resistance R_T*. Parallel–parallel feedback defines this quantity and must always include an impedance element, such as R_F. For the feedback to be effective, the inequality $i_F \gg i_A$ must hold. This implies that the internal transfer resistance of the A amplifier (which for a single transistor is $- h_{fe}R_L$) must be much greater than R_F. If a transistor has an h_{fe} of 100, and R_L is 1 kΩ, the internal transfer resistance is $- 100$ kΩ. If R_F is 10 kΩ, the over-all transfer resistance would be $- 10$ kΩ, and would not change appreciably if h_{fe} varied, the performance being determined by the passive element. Increasing h_{fe} increases the precision to which the transfer resistance R_T is defined, but does not increase it beyond R_F.

Input resistance for parallel–parallel feedback

As in the parallel–series case, the parallel input provides a low input resistance. In Fig. 6.4a,

$$\frac{v_{in}}{i_{in}} = \frac{v_{in}}{i_F + i_A} = \frac{v_{in}}{i_A(1 + A_i\beta)}, \qquad (6.13)$$

$$= \frac{R_A}{1 + A_i\beta},$$

where A_i is the current gain, and β is the fraction of the output current fed back to the input. The amplifier input resistance is reduced by the parallel input connection.

(d) *Series–series feedback*

From Fig. 6.4b, the input voltage

$$v_{in} = v_A + v_R \doteqdot v_R,$$

if the amplifier transfer conductance, i_o/v_A, is sufficiently large. Since $i_o \doteqdot v_R/R_F$,

$$\frac{i_o}{v_{in}} = \frac{1}{R_F} \quad \text{(or } G_F\text{).} \tag{6.14}$$

The feedback element, R_F, thus defines the *Transfer Conductance* for a series–series system.

Input resistance for series–series feedback

From Fig. 6.4b,

$$v_{in} = v_A + v_R = v_A(1 + A\beta), \tag{6.15}$$

if the transistor output voltage is assumed to be Av_A, and v_R is a fraction β of it. The input resistance of the feedback system is

$$\frac{v_{in}}{i_{in}} = \frac{v_A(1 + A\beta)}{i_{in}},$$

$$= R_A(1 + A\beta). \tag{6.16}$$

The input resistance is increased from R_A, the input resistance of the A amplifier, to the product of R_A and the loop gain.

Table 6.1. Characteristics of feedback systems

Feedback type	(a) Series–parallel	(b) Parallel–series	(c) Parallel–parallel	(d) Series–series
Defined parameter	Voltage gain	Current gain	Transfer impedance	Transfer conductance
Input resistance	High	Low	Low	High
Output resistance	Low	High	Low	High

Summary
The four basic feedback connections each define a different property. Parallel connection gives a low input or output resistance, while the series connection provides high resistance. Table 6.1 lists these relationships.

6.3. Examples of series–parallel feedback systems

6.3.1. Emitter follower buffer amplifier

The emitter follower, being a series–parallel amplifier with voltage gain close to unity, and having high input and low output resistance, performs well as a buffer stage.

As shown in § 6.2(a), over a wide range of load resistance,

$$R_{in} \doteqdot h_{fe}R_L, \tag{6.7}$$

where h_{fe} is the current gain.

Thus, for $h_{fe} = 100$ and $R_L = 1\,k\Omega$, R_{in} is approximately $100\,k\Omega$. Similarly, for the output resistance,

$$R_o \doteqdot R_s/h_{fe},$$

where R_s is the source resistance.

Because of the current gain, the input current is $1/h_{fe}$ times that at the output. The voltage gain is close to unity.

$$A \doteqdot \frac{h_{fe}R_L}{h_{ie} + h_{fe}R_L} \quad \text{(from Table 1.2)}.$$

For $R_L = 1\,k\Omega$, $h_{ie} = 2\,k\Omega$, $h_{fe} = 100$ and the emitter current $I_E = 1\,mA$,

$$A = \frac{100 \times 10^3}{2 \times 10^3 + 100 \times 10^3} = 0.98.$$

For large operating currents, h_{ie} is reduced and the gain approaches even more closely to unity. However, the direct base–emitter voltage necessary for the higher current increases with the larger current, consequently lowering the emitter voltage.

Design considerations for the emitter follower

Because it is a negative feedback connection, the design is straightforward. The emitter current will be that demanded by the voltage across the load, which closely follows the input voltage.

Thus, in Fig. 6.7, if v_{in} is 4.5 V, allowing 0.5 V across the base–emitter junction, the output voltage is 4 V. If the required operating current is 2 mA, the load resistor

$$R_L = \frac{V_L}{I_E} = \frac{4 \text{ V}}{2 \text{ mA}} = 2 \text{ k}\Omega.$$

The standing current is determined by the direct base voltage and load resistance. The transistor will always try to supply the demanded current, even though this could bring the device into the region of excessive dissipation. If there is a possibility of the emitter being accidentally grounded, thus reducing the load resistance to zero and thereby demanding a large current, the dissipation can be limited by a resistor in the collector connection.

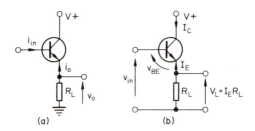

Fig. 6.7. The basic emitter follower or common collector amplifier.

Provision of base voltage for the emitter follower

For some applications, as in Fig. 6.8, where the base of the emitter follower is connected directly to the collector of the preceding stage, it is not necessary to make any special provision for the base voltage. However, if the emitter follower is capacitor coupled some provision must be made, preferably not affecting the desirable signal properties. Three methods are shown in Fig. 6.9.

The base current bias method of Fig. 6.9a has only limited control over the direct emitter voltage, but the negative feedback implicit with R_E ensures that it does not vary widely. If the large signal gain

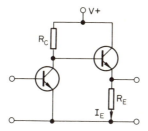

Fig. 6.8. A direct-coupled emitter follower stage.

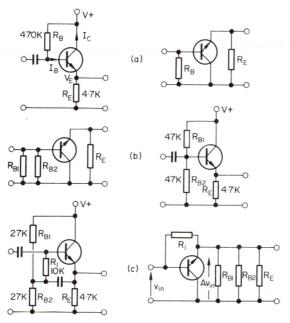

Fig. 6.9. Three bias methods for the emitter follower and their associated small-signal networks.

h_{FE} increases, the emitter current does not increase in proportion, since the emitter voltage will rise, thereby reducing the base current to the value necessary to maintain the emitter current V_E/R_E. If the base–emitter voltage V_{BE} is neglected, the standing currents are

$$i_B \doteqdot \frac{V - V_E}{R_B} \quad \text{and} \quad i_C \doteqdot \frac{V_E}{R_E},$$

where V is the positive voltage supply $V+$. As $i_C = h_{FE}i_B$,

$$\frac{V - V_E}{R_B} h_{FE} = \frac{V_E}{R_E},$$

whence

$$V_E = \frac{V h_{FE}}{\dfrac{R_B}{R_E} + h_{FE}}.$$

Differentiatng with respect to h_{FE}, to find the effect of a change in h_{FE},

$$\frac{dV_E}{dh_{FE}} = \frac{V\left(\dfrac{R_B}{R_E} + h_{FE}\right) - V h_{FE}}{\left(\dfrac{R_B}{R_E} + h_{FE}\right)^2} = \frac{V\dfrac{R_B}{R_E}}{\left(\dfrac{R_B}{R_E} + h_{FE}\right)^2},$$

$$= \frac{V_E \dfrac{R_B}{R_E}}{h_{FE}\left(\dfrac{R_B}{R_E} + h_{FE}\right)},$$

since,

$$\frac{V}{\dfrac{R_B}{R_E} + h_{FE}} = \frac{V_E}{h_{FE}}.$$

The fractional change in V_E, due to a change in h_{FE} is

$$\frac{dV_E}{V_E} = \frac{1}{1 + \dfrac{h_{FE}R_E}{R_B}} \cdot \frac{dh_{FE}}{h_{FE}}. \tag{6.17}$$

For Fig. 6.9a, where $h_{FE} = 100$, and $R_E/R_B = 1/100$, the fractional change in direct output voltage is half that of the current gain.

Greater stability is obtained with the arrangement of Fig. 6.9b, where the base current is assumed to be supplied from a resistor equivalent to R_{B1} and R_{B2} in parallel.

Thus, $R_E/R_B \doteqdot 1/5$ and

$$\frac{dV_E}{V_E} = \frac{1}{20}\frac{dh_{FE}}{h_{FE}}.$$

However, this arrangement reduces the effective input resistance since the two bias resistors directly shunt the input. If the high input resistance of the emitter follower is to be preserved, the arrangement of Fig. 6.9c can be used. Again $R_B \doteqdot 25 \text{ k}\Omega$, but the effective input resistance is increased since R_1 is, at signal frequencies, the only element connected to the base. The voltage across R_1 is $v_{in} - Av_{in}$ and the resistor will pass a current

$$i_R = \frac{(1-A)v_{in}}{R_1} = \frac{0.02\,v_{in}}{10\text{ k}\Omega},$$

for $A = 0.98$, as before. The effective value of R_1, apparent at the input of the amplifier, is

$$\frac{v_{in}}{i_R} = 500 \text{ k}\Omega.$$

As the input resistance of the transistor, operating as an emitter follower, is approximately $h_{fe}R_L = 470 \text{ k}\Omega$ for $h_{fe} = 100$, the estimated input resistance of the system is $R_{in} \doteqdot 250 \text{ k}\Omega$.

Input capacitance of the emitter follower
    The effect of base–emitter capacitance on the amplifier input admittance is modified in a manner similar to the effect of R_1, in Fig. 6.9c. In Fig. 6.10a, current $i_2 = sC_{be}(v_{in} - v_o)$. The total input capacitive current is

$$i_c = i_1 + i_2 = sC_{bc}v_{in} + (1-A)sC_{be}v_{in},$$

where A is close to unity. The effective input capacitance is thus,

$$C_{in} = C_{bc} + (1-A)C_{be}. \tag{6.18}$$

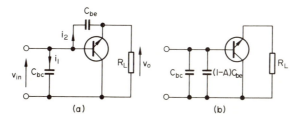

(a)   (b)

Fig. 6.10. Input capacitance relationships for the emitter follower.

Typical values are $C_{bc} = 2\,\text{pF}$, and $C_{be} = 30\,\text{pF}$, so the input capacitance will be essentially due to the latter term. It will be much less than for the common emitter amplifier where

$$C_{in} = C_{be} + (1 - A)C_{bc}, \qquad (6.19)$$

and A is negative and often much greater than unity. This enhancement is referred to as "Miller effect", and can considerably modify high frequency performance.

Maximum value of input resistance for the emitter follower

It is shown in the performance curve for the input resistance of an emitter follower that a maximum value is attained, after which further increase in R_L has no effect. This maximum value is apparent if the common base equivalent h network is drawn, as in Fig. 6.11. It is obvious that when R_L is infinite and i_e is zero, the base and collector are shunted by h_{ob}.

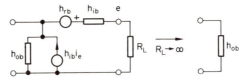

Fig. 6.11. The common base equivalent network for the emitter follower, and the form for R_L infinite.

In terms of common emitter parameters,

$$R_{in(max)} = \frac{1}{h_{ob}} = \frac{1 - h_{re} + h_{fe} + \Delta h}{h_{oe}}. \qquad (6.20)$$

6.3.2. Output stage for a direct-coupled amplifier

The emitter follower can be used to provide the required output current from a low impedance source.

Example

Basic emitter follower. The transistor is selected to have the necessary power rating, and the value of the emitter resistor, R_E in Fig. 6.12, must be calculated for correct operation.

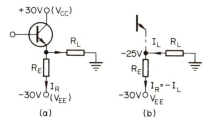

Fig. 6.12. (a) Direct-coupled emitter follower currents and (b) showing the voltages and currents when the output voltage is minimum.

The supply voltages are $+30$ V and -30 V, the load resistance is 5 kΩ and the maximum output voltage 25 V. The maximum load current is thus,

$$I_{L(\text{max})} = \frac{V_{L(\text{max})}}{R_L} = \frac{25 \text{ V}}{5 \text{ k}\Omega} = 5 \text{ mA}.$$

When the output voltage V_L is at its minimum value of -25 V, the load current must pass through R_E, and the transistor supplies no current. This condition, illustrated in Fig. 6.12b, determines the maximum value for R_E.

$$R_E = \frac{V_{L(\text{min})} - V_{EE}}{I_L} = \frac{-25 \text{ V} - (-30 \text{ V})}{5 \text{ mA}} = 1 \text{ k}\Omega.$$

Generally, the transistor supplies current to both the load R_L, and to R_E. Thus,

$$I_E = I_L + I_R = \frac{V_L}{R_L} + \frac{V_L - V_{EE}}{R_E}.$$

Power dissipation

The dissipation is mainly at the base–collector junction, where the voltage is a maximum.

$$P_C \doteqdot V_{CE} I_C,$$

$$= (V_{CC} - V_L)\left[\frac{V_L}{R_L} + \frac{V_L - V_{EE}}{R_E}\right],$$

$$= (V_{CC} - V_L)\left[\frac{V_L(R_E + R_L)}{R_E R_L} - \frac{V_{EE}}{R_E}\right].$$

Differentiating P_C with respect to V_L to find the voltage for maximum power dissipation,

$$\frac{dP_C}{dV_L} = \frac{R_E + R_L}{R_E R_L} V_{CC} - \frac{2V_L(R_E + R_L)}{R_E R_L} + \frac{V_{EE}}{R_E},$$

$$= \frac{V_{CC}}{R_L} - 2V_L \frac{R_E + R_L}{R_E R_L} \quad \text{(as } V_{EE} = -V_{CC}\text{)},$$

$$= 0 \quad \text{for maximum (or minimum).}$$

Thus, the output voltage at which power dissipation is a maximum,

$$V_{L(\text{max } P_C)} = \frac{V_{CC} R_E}{2(R_E + R_L)} = \frac{30 \text{ V}}{2} \times \frac{1 \text{ k}\Omega}{(5+1) \text{ k}\Omega} = 2.5 \text{ V}.$$

For V_L greater than this value, I_E is larger but V_{CE} is reduced. For smaller output voltages the reverse is the case,

$$P_{C(\text{max})} = (V_{CC} - V'_L)\left[\frac{V'_L - V_{EE}}{R_E} + \frac{V'_L}{R_L}\right],$$

where V'_L is the load voltage for maximum dissipation,

$$P_{C(\text{max})} = (27.5 \text{ V}) \quad \times (27.5 \text{ mA} + 0.5 \text{ mA})$$

$$\underset{\substack{\text{Transistor} \\ \text{voltage}}}{} \times \left(\underset{\text{in } R_E}{\text{Current}} + \underset{\text{in load}}{\text{Current}}\right)$$

$$= 0.77 \text{ W}.$$

A 1-watt transistor is required.

It is apparent that the principal current component is that drawn by R_E, and not the external load current. It is possible to reduce the former using methods which will now be described.

Emitter follower with emitter current source

If the emitter resistor R_E is replaced by a current source to supply the 5 mA required for I_R, the power requirements are considerably reduced. This current is needed when the output voltage is at its minimum, and the maximum load current is supplied from V_{EE} as in Fig. 6.12b.

Emitter follower as a current source

If the input voltage to an emitter follower is held constant, the emitter voltage will be of a similar value, and the collector current is then determined by the emitter resistor,

$$I_C \doteqdot \frac{V_B - V_{BE}}{R_E}.$$

The constant current network is shown in Fig. 6.13. From this, the collector power dissipation

$$P_C \doteqdot V_{CE}(I_R + I_L) = (V_{CC} - V_L)\left(I_R + \frac{V_L}{R_L}\right).$$

$$\frac{dP_C}{dV_L} = \frac{V_{CC}}{R_L} - I_R - 2\frac{V_I}{R_L}.$$

$$V'_L = V_{L(\max P_C)} = \frac{V_{CC}}{2} - \frac{I_R R_L}{2} = \frac{30\ V}{2} - \frac{5\ mA \times 5\ k\Omega}{2} = 2.5\ V.$$

$$P_{C(\max)} = (V_{CC} - V'_L)\left[I_R + \frac{V'_L}{R_L}\right],$$

$$= (30\ V - 2.5\ V)\left(5\ mA + \frac{2.5\ V}{5\ k\Omega}\right) = 0.151\ mW.$$

This is considerably less than the power requirement for the previous case.

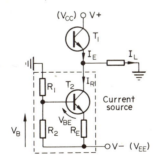

Fig. 6.13. Emitter follower with current source.

Design of current source

As the minimum value of output voltage is -25 V, the collector voltage of T_2 should not rise above -27 V. Let $V_B = 3$ V ($R_1 = 27$ kΩ and $R_2 = 3$ kΩ, for $V_{EE} = -30$ V), then the voltage across R_E is approximately 2.5 V for a silicon transistor. Thus,

$$R_E = \frac{3\text{ V}}{5\text{ mA}} = 600\ \Omega.$$

A 560-Ω resistor, which is a preferred value, would ensure satisfactory operation.

Complementary emitter follower stage

In the previous example much of the power dissipated by T_1 is due to the 5 mA drawn by the current source. By using two emitter followers, one operating for positive output voltages and the other for negative, the standing current is no longer required.

In Fig. 6.14a when V_L is positive, T_1 supplies the load current, and for V_L negative, T_2 draws current through R_L. Note that T_2 is a *pnp*

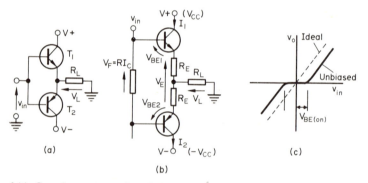

Fig. 6.14. Complementary emitter follower stage, (a) without forward bias, (b) with forward bias and (c) its transfer characteristic.

transistor. When v_{in} is zero, both transistors are non-conducting as neither has the necessary forward bias. With germanium transistors the difference in input voltage for conduction, ($V_{BE(ON)}$ in Fig. 6.14c) is ± 0.15 V, but for silicon devices the gap is widened to ± 0.5 V. While this non-conducting region is undesirable in linear amplifiers, it does not affect operation of switching systems. For linear amplifiers it is desirable that both devices should be conducting for $v_{in} = 0$, so that the change over from one device to the other is accomplished smoothly. By separating the bases with a voltage V_F, which is somewhat greater than the sum of the "on" voltages, the difference is available to define the emitter currents, and consequently the collector currents I_1 and I_2 in Fig. 6.14b. There are three conditions of operation:

(1) $V_L = 0$.   Both transistors are conducting ($I_1 = I_2 = V_E/2R_E$, where $V_E = V_L - V_{BE1} + V_{BE2}$). R_E is chosen to provide a reasonable standing current, usually considerably less than $I_{L(max)}$.

(2) $V_L > 0$.   Load current flows through the upper emitter resistor, increasing the voltage across it, thereby reducing the voltage available to the lower resistor, and consequently reducing I_2. At some larger value of V_L, $I_1 R_E = V_F - V_{BE1}$, and T_2 will no longer be forward biased and will stop conducting. The load current is now equal to I_1, and the total dissipation is

$$I_L(V_{CC} - V_L) = \frac{V_L}{R_L}(V_{CC} - V_L).$$

(3) $V_L < 0$.   The load current is supplied by T_2.

Power dissipation $P_C \fallingdotseq V_{CE}I_C$,

$$\fallingdotseq (V_{CC} - V_L)\frac{V_L}{R_L},$$

if small voltages are neglected.

$$\frac{dP_C}{dV_L} = \frac{V_{CC} - 2V_L}{R_L},$$

or,

$$V_{L(max\ PC)} = V_{CC}^2,$$

whence,

$$P_{C(max)} = \frac{V_{CC}^2}{4R_L}.$$

For supply voltages of ± 30 V and $R_L = 5$ kΩ, the maximum collector dissipation is $P_{C(max)} = 0.045$ W.

A low-power transistor may therefore be used in place of the medium-power device. If the forward voltage V_F, in Fig. 6.14b, is 1.5 V, and the conducting base–emitter voltages are 0.6 V, the voltage V_E across the emitter resistors is 0.3 V. The

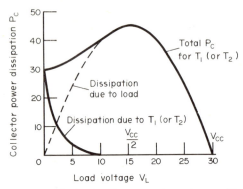

Fig. 6.15. Collector dissipation for a complementary emitter follower.

emitter current is $I_E = V_E/2R_E$, so for an emitter current of 1 mA, $R_E = 150\,\Omega$. Figure 6.15 shows that dissipation is comparatively high for zero V_L. This is because, although the current is only 1 mA, the full voltage is across the transistor. The relatively small value for R_E ensures that the voltage across it is only 0.75 V at full load.

Compound emitter follower—Darlington connection

So far, the transistor has only been required to dissipate the required power. However, a further consideration is the necessary input current, since this can modify the performance of the previous stage. The current gain h_{fe} is typically 100, implying that the input current is 1/100 of the output current. However, this can be reduced by directly coupling another emitter follower stage, as in Fig. 6.16a. The effect of this is to increase the current gain from h_{fe} to $h_{fe1} \times h_{fe2}$, i.e. the product of the individual gains. Figure 6.16b shows how the collector characteristic is modified when the two devices are combined. The first transistor will often be operating at low current levels, where its performance is rather poor. This can be improved by the presence of R_B in Fig. 6.16a which, because it has the relatively constant base–emitter voltage of T_2 across it, draws a nominally constant current from T_1. The emitter current for $R_B = 10\,\mathrm{k\Omega}$ and T_2 a silicon transistor, would be

$$I_E = \frac{V_{BE}}{R_B} = \frac{0.6\,\mathrm{V}}{10\,\mathrm{k\Omega}} = 60\,\mu\mathrm{A}.$$

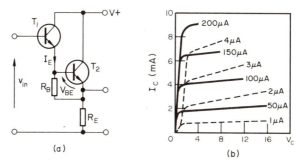

(a)

(b)

Fig. 6.16. (a) Direct-coupled Darlington stage. (b) Collector characteristic for the compound connection. Solid lines represent base current for a single device, and broken lines for the Darlington.

6.3.3. Augmented emitter follower

The use of complementary transistors enables a compound emitter follower to be formed, which has properties similar to those of the *Darlington connection*. The arrangement is shown in Fig. 6.17a, and it is apparent that there is only one base–emitter voltage step between input and output. This can be a desirable feature. The second transistor T_2 acts as a common emitter stage, augmenting the emitter current of T_1. Current gain is similar to that for the Darlington connection, i.e. the product of the individual gains, but has lower input and output resistances. The combination tends to operate more as a "super" emitter follower, in which the input and output resistances are proportional to the load and source resistances, than as a Darlington which has more constant performance characteristics. Figure 6.17b shows another complementary connec-

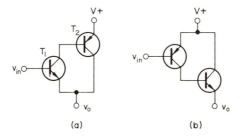

(a)

(b)

Fig. 6.17. Compound complementary stages. (a) Augmented emitter follower. (b) Common emitter–common collector.

tion. This is not strictly an emitter follower, but is a common emitter stage followed by an emitter follower. While having the output properties of the latter, the input stage has the low input resistance of a common emitter stage, signal inversion and voltage gain.

6.3.4.   Field effect source follower

The bipolar junction transistor is forward biased and always requires some base current when operating. In applications where this is undesirable a field effect transistor may be used. Figure 6.18 shows how such a device could be used to monitor the voltage in a capacitor. The reverse biased input junction of the FET passes a current of approximately 10^{-9} A, and has much less effect on the capacitor charge than would a forward biased junction bipolar transistor. The system of Fig. 6.18 has several disadvantages.

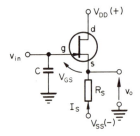

Fig. 6.18.   Monitoring a capacitor voltage with a FET source follower.

(a) The gate–source voltage varies with input voltage, thereby reducing linearity (see Fig. 6.20).
(b) Output voltage is positive with respect to the gate voltage.
(c) Gain is somewhat less than that of a bipolar transistor.
(d) The maximum current which can be passed is that when the gate–source voltage is zero (I_{DSS}). This is 4.25 mA for the device whose characteristics are shown in Fig. 6.19.
A bipolar transistor is not limited in this way, and will always endeavour to pass the demanded current.

Relation between input and output voltage

$$V_{in} = V_{GS} + V_o = V_{GS} + I_S R_S.$$

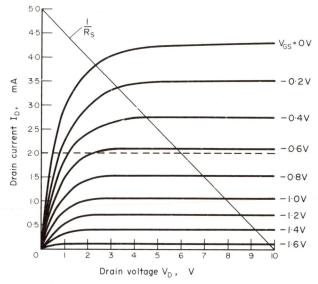

Fig. 6.19. Output characteristic for a 2N 3819 FET.

If V_{SS} is -5 V, V_{DD} is $+5$ V and $R_S = 2$ kΩ, Table 6.2 can be created and Fig. 6.20 drawn.

Operation with constant current

If the device is operated with the source resistor replaced by a current sink, the gate–source voltage, V_{GS}, will remain constant for the range of input voltages. The broken line on Fig. 6.19 indicates the path of operation for $I_D = 2$ mA, where $V_{GS} \doteqdot -0.6$ V.

Table 6.2

$V_{GS}(V)$	$I_D = I_S\,(\text{mA})$	$V_0 = I_S R_S\,(V)$	$V_{in} = V_{GS} + V_0$
-1.6	0.2	0.4	-1.2
-1.4	0.4	0.8	-0.6
-1.2	0.75	1.5	0.3
-1.0	1.1	2.2	1.2
-0.8	1.5	3.0	2.2
-0.6	2.15	4.3	3.7
-0.4	2.75	5.5	5.1
-0.2	3.4	6.8	6.6
0	3.8	7.6	7.6

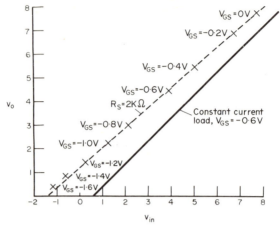

Fig. 6.20. Transfer characteristic for the source followers of Figs. 6.18 and 6.21.

Current sink

A current sink of 2 mA can be formed using a FET with a source resistor

$$R_S = \frac{V_{GS}}{I_S} = \frac{0.6 \text{ V}}{2 \text{ mA}} \doteq 310 \text{ }\Omega.$$

Offsetting the gate–source voltage

The source of T_1 in Fig. 6.21a is 0.62 V positive with respect to the input voltage. A 500-Ω resistor has 1 volt developed across it by the

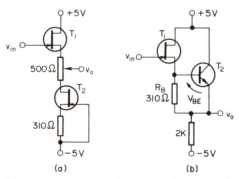

Fig. 6.21. Source followers with current sinks. (a) FET current sink, (b) relatively constant current drawn by V_{BE}/R_B.

2-mA source current, and part of this can be used to offset the gate–source voltage. Alternatively, the method shown in Fig. 6.21b can be used, where a bipolar transistor T_2 provides a low output resistance as an emitter follower. It also maintains a relatively constant voltage across R_B, thus drawing the required current from the source T_1. If R_B is variable, the offset between output and input can be brought to zero.

6.3.5. Operational amplifier voltage follower

A very convenient form of voltage follower can readily be obtained using an operational amplifier with series–parallel feedback of unity, as in Fig. 6.22. The input voltage to the amplifier is $(v_{in} - v_o)$ and the output votage,

$$v_o = A(v_{in} - v_o),$$

or

$$\frac{v_o}{v_{in}} = \frac{A}{1 + A}. \qquad (6.21)$$

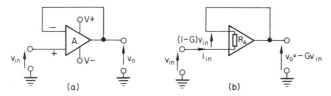

Fig. 6.22. Operational amplifier connected as a voltage follower (a), and determination of its input resistance (b).

The voltage gain A is very high for such amplifiers, being typically 10^5, and yielding for the follower a gain of

$$G = \frac{10^5}{100,001} = 0.99999.$$

It is more convenient to express the performance in terms of error. Thus

$$\frac{v_o}{v_{in}} = \frac{1}{1 + 1/A} \doteqdot 1(1 - 1/A),$$

using the binomial expansion approximation

$$1/(1+x) \doteqdot (1-x) \text{ if } x \ll 1. \tag{6.22}$$

The fractional error is $1/A$ and equals 10^{-5} (or 10^{-3} %). It is apparent that the voltage gain is much closer to unity than that of an emitter follower.

Operational amplifier follower frequency response

The variation of gain with frequency for a general-purpose operational amplifier takes the form shown in Fig. 6.23. When both voltage gain and frequency are plotted on the same logarithmic scale, the response is a straight line from the upper bandwidth limit,

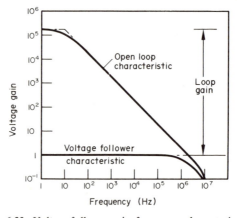

Fig. 6.23. Voltage follower gain–frequency characteristic.

or corner frequency, at approximately 10 Hz, to below unity gain. This characteristic is specially designed to enable operation in the feedback mode to be free from oscillation. It is apparent that the bandwidth of the open-loop amplifier, i.e. the amplifier with no feedback, is small. However, as shown in § 6.1, the application of negative feedback extends the bandwidth by the factor $(1 + A\beta)$, or in the case of the follower where $\beta = 1$, by $(1 + A)$. As A is 10^5 the bandwidth is extended from the open-loop value of 10 Hz to 1 MHz. The closed-loop voltage follower response is drawn as a horizontal line on the unity gain axis, meeting the open-loop curve at the closed-loop bandwidth upper frequency. As shown in Fig. 6.23 for the voltage follower, the loop gain equals the gain of the A amplifier. The *gain–bandwidth product* of the amplifier (i.e. the low-frequency gain multiplied by the 3-dB bandwidth, or the bandwidth at unity gain) is equal to the voltage follower bandwidth.

Input resistance

As the voltage follower is a series–parallel arrangement, the amplifier input resistance R_A is increased by the feedback connection. Specifically, the voltage across R_A, in Fig. 6.22b, is $v_{in} - Gv_{in}$, where $G = 1/(1 + 1/A)$. The input current,

$$i_{in} = \frac{1 - G}{R_A} v_{in},$$

and

$$R_{in} = \frac{v_{in}}{i_{in}} = \frac{R_A}{1 - G}.$$

As G is very close to unity, the denominator term is small and the input resistance is extremely large. The gain for the follower has been calculated as 0.99999, so for a typical amplifier input resistance R_A of 100 kΩ,

$$R_{in} = \frac{100 \text{ k}\Omega}{1 - 0.99999} = 10,000 \text{ M}\Omega.$$

However, such an extremely high resistance would probably be reduced by leakage resistance paths. Also, at frequencies above 10 Hz the gain falls as indicated in Fig. 6.23, and the input resistance falls. Unless the operational amplifier has a FET input, base current must be supplied; for a general purpose amplifier this will be of the order of 10^{-7} A, and is called the *input bias current*.

Offset voltage

Operational amplifiers are direct coupled and, ideally, for zero input voltage the output voltage should also be zero. In practice it never is, and any deviation from zero is the *output offset voltage*. It is usually related to the lack of symmetry in the manufacture of the input stages.

It is convenient to define performance, however, in terms of the

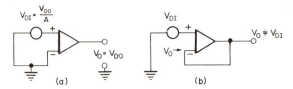

Fig. 6.24. (a) V_{DI} is the hypothetical voltage source necessary to form the offset voltage V_{DO}. (b) After the feedback connection is made the output voltage $V_o \doteq V_{DI}$.

input referred offset or, more briefly, the input offset voltage. As shown in Fig. 6.24, this is the output voltage, when the input is grounded, divided by the voltage gain. Alternatively it can be regarded as the input voltage necessary to bring the output to zero. The input offset voltage is usually several millivolts for an operational amplifier. If the input offset was 1 mV, for an A gain of 10^5 the output offset would be 100 V. However, the feedback connection considerably reduces this figure. Referring to Fig. 6.24b, the effective input voltage is $V_{DI} - V_o$. The output voltage is then

$$V_o = A(V_{DI} - V_o) = \frac{AV_{DI}}{1+A} \doteq V_{DI}.$$

The output offset is thus the same as the input referred voltage offset. While V_{DI} is a hypothetical voltage source it can nevertheless be measured, by using the voltage follower connection and measuring the output voltage. The feedback produces a voltage which opposes the effect of the input referred offset and is thus equal to it.

Output resistance

An operational amplifier without feedback has a typical output resistance R_{Ao} of about 100-Ω. With series–parallel feedback this is reduced.

From eqn. (6.8),

$$R_{out} = \frac{R_A}{1+A\beta} = \frac{R_{A0}}{1+A\beta} \quad \text{for the voltage follower,}$$

$$\doteq \frac{100\Omega}{10^5} = 1 \text{ m}\Omega.$$

6.3.6. Applications of the voltage follower

(a) *Buffer amplifier*

The operational amplifier voltage follower has excellent characteristics for this type of operation, since it has high input resistance, low output resistance, and a voltage gain close to unity.

Example

Parallel "T" filter. Figure 6.25 shows a parallel "T" network, and its frequency response plotted on a universal frequency axis.

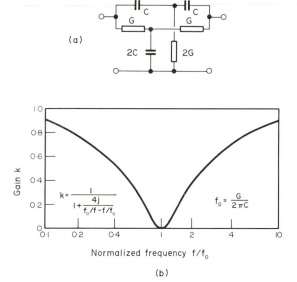

Fig. 6.25. (a) Parallel "T" network and (b) its normalized amplitude response.

The voltage follower can be used as a buffer between the network and a load, as in Fig. 6.26,

$$v_0 = A\,(kv_{in} - v_0),$$

where k represents the response of the network,

$$v_o\,(1 + A) = Akv_{in},$$

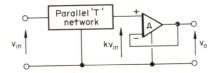

Fig. 6.26. Voltage follower as a buffer for the parallel "T" network.

or,

$$\frac{v_o}{v_{in}} = \frac{Ak}{1+A} = \frac{k}{1+1/A} \doteq k, \quad \text{if } A \gg 1.$$

As expected, the amplifier simply performs as an accurate voltage follower. The network acts as a tuned rejection filter, with a rejection frequency of $f_o = 1/(2\pi RC)$. Its response is described by

$$k = \frac{1}{1+\dfrac{4j}{(\omega/\omega_0)-(\omega_0/\omega)}} = \frac{1}{1+\dfrac{4j}{y}}$$

where

$$y = \frac{\omega}{\omega_0} - \frac{\omega_0}{\omega}.$$

This response is similar in form to that of a series resonant LCR network, where the output voltage is obtained from across the resistor. For such a network,

$$k' = \frac{1}{1+jQ\left(\dfrac{\omega}{\omega_0} - \dfrac{\omega_0}{\omega}\right)} = \frac{1}{1+jQy}.$$

This has a maximum of unity at the resonant frequency, ω_0, and is zero for very high and very low frequencies, which is the opposite of the curve for the parallel "T" network of Fig. 6.25. However, the 3-dB bandwidth, where the response is 0.7 of the maximum, is given for the above equation when

$$\frac{1}{|1+jQy_1|} = \frac{1}{\sqrt{2}} \quad \text{(the "half-power" condition)}$$

or

$$1+(Qy_1)^2 = 2,$$

and

$$\pm y_1 = 1/Q,$$

where

$$y_1 = \frac{\omega_1}{\omega_0} - \frac{\omega_0}{\omega_1} \quad \text{and} \quad -y_1 = \frac{\omega_2}{\omega_0} - \frac{\omega_0}{\omega_2},$$

define the bandwidth $\omega_1 - \omega_2$ or $f_1 - f_2$.

By analogy, the parallel "T" network has a Q of 1/4, and a bandwidth of approximately $8f_o$. This can be found from Fig. 6.25b.

(b) High Q operation using boot-strap connection

If the arrangement of Fig. 6.26 is modified to that of Fig. 6.27, the bandwidth of the parallel "T" network is reduced, and the effective Q is increased.

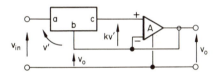

Fig. 6.27. Boot-strap operation.

The common terminal of the network is, in this case, connected to the output terminal instead of to ground, and its voltage rises with the follower input voltage. If the follower gain is unity, the voltage kv is kept at zero by the amplifier operation. This type of operation is called *boot strapping*, terminal b being raised by its own "boot straps". Analysing Fig. 6.27,

$$v_o = kv', \quad \text{where } v' = v_{in} - v_o,$$
$$= Ak(v_{in} - v_o),$$

or

$$\frac{v_o}{v_{in}} = \frac{Ak}{1 + Ak} = \frac{1}{1 + 1/Ak}.$$

This is unity for $k = 1$, zero for $k = 0$, but approximately equal to Ak when k is small (i.e. $0 \leqslant Ak \ll 1$).

Substituting $k = \dfrac{1}{1 + 4j/y}$ yields

$$\frac{v_o}{v_{in}} = \frac{A}{A + 1 + \dfrac{4j}{y}}.$$

The modulus of this expression is equal to $1/\sqrt{2}$ at the bandwidth half power frequencies. Thus,

$$\frac{A^2}{(A + 1)^2 + \left(\dfrac{4}{y_1}\right)^2} = \frac{1}{2}.$$

Since the gain of the operational amplifier is much greater than unity,

$$y_1 \doteqdot \frac{4}{A}.$$

For high Q systems,

$$y_1 = \frac{\omega_1}{\omega_0} - \frac{\omega_0}{\omega_1} = \frac{\omega_1{}^2 - \omega_0{}^2}{\omega_0 \omega_1} = \frac{(\omega_1 - \omega_0)(\omega_1 + \omega_0)}{\omega_0 \omega_1},$$

$$\doteqdot \frac{2(\omega_1 - \omega_0)}{\omega_0{}^2} \doteqdot \frac{1}{Q},$$

where $2(\omega_1 - \omega_0)$ is the 3-dB bandwidth.

For the modified system of Fig. 6.27,

$$Q = \frac{1}{y_1} = \frac{A}{4}.$$

The Q can be very high. For instance, for $A = 10^5$, $Q = 2.5 \times 10^4$, and for $f_o = 1$ kHz, the bandwidth

$$\text{BW} = \frac{f_o}{Q} = \frac{10^3}{2.5 \times 10^4} = 0.04 \text{ Hz}.$$

DESIGN EXAMPLE 6.1

Required, a parallel "T", band rejection filter with centre frequency of 1 kHz, and bandwidth variable from 1 Hz to 100 Hz.

Required Q. The maximum value required is

$$Q = \frac{f_o}{BW} = \frac{1000}{1.0} = 10^3.$$

Required amplifier gain $A = Q \times 4 = 4 \times 10^3$.

Most operational amplifiers have voltage gains considerably in excess of this figure. For instance, the 741 amplifier has a typical gain of 2×10^5, with a minimum value of 2.5×10^4.

Parallel "T" elements.

$$\omega_0 = 2\pi f_o = 2\pi \times 10^3 \text{ rad/s.}$$

As the centre frequency must be accurately defined for operation with the narrow bandwidth specified, a value of C well above the stray shunt capacitance should be chosen.

Let $C = 0.1 \ \mu\text{F} = 10^{-7} \text{ F.}$

$$R = \frac{1}{\omega_0 C} = \frac{1}{2\pi \times 10^3 \times 10^{-7}} = 1.59 \text{ k}\Omega.$$

For precise operation, high stability components should be used and values checked on a bridge. Resistor values of $1.58 \text{ k}\Omega$ and $1.60 \text{ k}\Omega$ are available as standard precision elements.

Control of Q. The potentiometer shown in Fig. 6.28 effectively controls the gain of the amplifier and hence the Q. The 100-Ω resistor ensures that the amplifier gain is not reduced to zero.

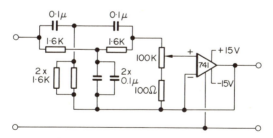

Fig. 6.28. Boot-strapped parallel "T".

(c) *Diode staircase generator*

An arrangement which is used for pulse counting, pulse-rate measurement, staircase generation and similar operations is shown

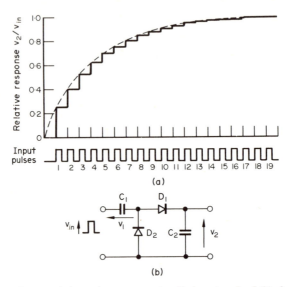

(a)

(b)

Fig. 6.29. (a) Output of the staircase generator diode network of (b), for $C_2 = 3C_1$. This is a much smaller ratio than is usual, and the initial step would normally be much smaller.

in Fig. 6.29. Capacitors C_1 and C_2 are charged through diode D_1 by positive pulses. As the voltage is shared inversely with capacitance values,

$$\frac{V_1}{V_2} = \frac{C_2}{C_1}.$$

If C_1 is made smaller than C_2, the latter will receive only a small part of the voltage pulse. As the pulse returns to zero, C_1 is discharged but the charge remains on C_2. The second input voltage pulse adds further to this charge. However, as the voltage on C_2 builds up, it subtracts from the input voltage. The full value is no longer available for charging, and the steps become exponentially smaller. The maximum voltage to which C_2 can be charged is V_{in}.

If, as in Fig. 6.30, the anode of D_2 is returned to the output of a voltage follower, at the termination of an input pulse C_1 charges through D_2 to the same voltage as C_2. As the two capacitors have the same voltage but opposite sign, they cancel each other and permit the full input voltage to be applied at each input pulse. Each step of

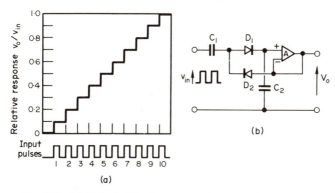

Fig. 6.30. (a) Output of the boot-strapped system of network (b).

voltage on C_2 is now of equal magnitude, and the maximum voltage is not now limited to the amplitude of V_{in}. A further advantage of this arrangement is that the voltage follower acts as a buffer stage.

6.3.7. The voltage amplifier using operational amplifiers

A simple voltage amplifier arrangement can be formed by modifying the basic voltage follower connection of Fig. 6.22a. In Fig. 6.31 the feedback network is a potentiometer which supplies a fraction β of the output voltage to the input. The input voltage to the A amplifier is $v_{in} - \beta v_o$ and $v_o = A(v_{in} - \beta v_o)$. Thus,

$$\frac{v_o}{v_{in}} = \frac{A}{1 + A\beta} \doteqdot \frac{1}{\beta},\tag{6.23}$$

where the feedback fraction is

$$\beta = \frac{R_1}{R_1 + R_2}.$$

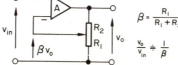

Fig. 6.31. Variable voltage gain amplifier. (Series–parallel.)

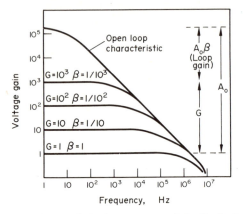

Fig. 6.32. Frequency characteristic for a range of feedback fractions β, of a series–parallel voltage amplifier.

As the feedback fraction is decreased the gain increases, but the loop gain falls, reducing the bandwidth for high gains. This effect is shown in Fig. 6.32. The closed-loop gain is

$$G = \frac{A}{1 + A\beta},$$

or,

$$\log G = \log A - \log (1 + A\beta),$$
$$\doteqdot \log A - \log A\beta.$$

As the gain–frequency curve is drawn with logarithmic axes, the closed-loop gain is found by subtracting the loop gain $A\beta$, from the A amplifier response. This relationship is satisfied if a horizontal line is drawn from the appropriate point on the gain axis, to meet the open-loop characteristic. The point of intersection is the bandwidth.

Performance precision

The feedback fraction β, is determined by the resistor potential divider of Fig. 6.31, i.e. $\beta = R_1/(R_1 + R_2)$. The closed-loop gain, from eqn. (6.23), is

$$G = \frac{A}{1 + A\beta} \doteqdot \frac{1}{\beta}\left(1 - \frac{1}{A\beta}\right).$$

In Fig. 6.32, for a closed-loop gain of 10^3, the loop gain $A\beta$ is approximately 2000, i.e. $A_o \times \beta$. The error term $1/A\beta$ is 5×10^{-4} (or 0.05%). When β is less than unity the input resistance will be lower, the output resistance higher and the offset greater, than for the voltage follower where $\beta = 1$.

Offset voltage for the voltage amplifier

The voltage follower diagram of Fig. 6.24b becomes that of Fig. 6.33 when β is not unity. Considering only the offset voltages, the input to the amplifier is $V_{DI} - \beta V_o$, where V_{DI} is the input referred offset. The output voltage due to the offset is $V_o = A(V_{DI} - \beta V_o)$, or

$$V_0 = \frac{V_{DI}A}{1 + A\beta} = V_{DI}G \doteq V_{DI}/\beta. \qquad (6.24)$$

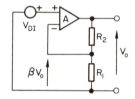

Fig. 6.33. Output voltage generated by the input offset. At the inverting input, $\beta v_o \doteq V_{DI}$.

The output offset is the input offset multiplied by the closed-loop gain, G. Thus, if G is 100 (i.e. $\beta = 1/100$), an input referred offset of 1 mV becomes an output offset of 100 mV. As with the voltage follower connection, a voltage equal to V_{DI} is produced at the inverting input. Some amplifiers have connections which make provision for an external network to be used to bring the output to zero. The input offset is a function of temperature, usually changing about 10 μV for each °C.

Slewing rate

When the input is a step voltage, as in Fig. 6.34, the output will rise as rapidly as possible, but, because of charging time constants within the amplifier, the response will be a ramp. The slope of this ramp is the amplifier *slewing rate*. For large output voltage swings (i.e. 20 V peak-to-peak) it is this effect which causes high frequency

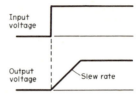

Fig. 6.34. Output response to an input step.

limitations rather than the frequency characteristic of Fig. 6.32. A typical figure for slewing rate is 1 V/μs. If an output sinewave has an amplitude of 10 V,

$$v_o = E \sin \omega t = 10 \sin \omega t.$$

The slope is found by differentiation,

$$\frac{dv_o}{dt} = E\omega \cos \omega t.$$

As $\cos \omega t$ has a maximum value of unity, the maximum slope is $E\omega$. The maximum frequency which can be handled is therefore

$$\omega_{max} = \frac{\text{Slew rate}}{E},$$

or,

$$f_{max} = \frac{\text{Slew rate}}{2\pi E} = \frac{10^6}{2\pi 10} \fallingdotseq 16 \text{ KHz},$$

if the above values are substituted. This could be a somewhat lower frequency than the small signal bandwidth limit.

Bias current

As discussed in § 6.3.6, for other than those with FET inputs, base current must be supplied to the two inputs of an operational amplifier. Consequently there should always be ohmic paths to these inputs, and the resistance to ground seen from them, should be the same. This ensures that the bias current produces equal voltages at the two inputs, which will subtract and not introduce an additional offset. In Fig. 6.35, a 10-kΩ resistor is inserted in the input path to provide a voltage drop equal to that across the parallel combination of R_1 and R_2. If this was not done, a bias current of 0.1 μA would

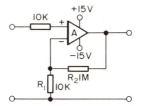

Fig. 6.35. Voltage amplifier with a gain of 100.

produce an additional offset of 1 mV. Differences in the two bias currents is the *current offset*, but this is not usually of great significance.

Example

Voltage amplifier with a gain of 100. The feedback fraction β must be 1/100 and the ratio of R_1 to R_2, in Fig. 6.35, should be 1/99. However, in most cases a ratio of 1/100 would be acceptable, so let $R_1 = 10 \text{ k}\Omega$ and $R_2 = 1 \text{ M}\Omega$. A 10-kΩ resistor is inserted in the input lead to match the bias–current voltage drop. From Fig. 6.32, the bandwidth is approximately 20 kHz and, for $R_A = 100 \text{ k}\Omega$ and $A_o\beta = 2000$, the input resistance $R_{in} = (1 + A_o\beta)R_{Ao} \doteqdot 200 \text{ M}\Omega$ at low frequency. The output resistance $R_{out} = R_{Ao}/(1 + A_o\beta) \doteqdot 0.05 \text{ }\Omega$.

6.3.8. Capacitor-coupled voltage amplifier

If the direct voltage component of an incoming signal is to be rejected, the voltage amplifier can be capacitor coupled, as in Fig. 6.36. This results in a low frequency cut-off, the frequency of which

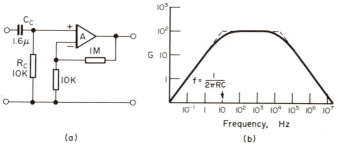

(a) (b)

Fig. 6.36. (a) Capacitor-coupled voltage amplifier and (b) its gain–frequency characteristic.

is determined by C_c and R_c. If the output offset is still required to be zero volts, R_c should be made equal to R_1 and R_2 is parallel. For operation down to 10 Hz,

$$C_c = \frac{1}{2\pi f R_c} = \frac{1}{2\pi \times 10 \times 10^4} = 1.59 \ \mu F.$$

If the resistance values of R_1 and R_2 are increased, say to 100 kΩ and 10 MΩ, respectively, R_c should be increased and C_c reduced. As the coupling network is not in the feedback loop, β does not affect the cut-off at low frequency. The input resistance is equal to R_c. For high-voltage gains, of the order of 1000, it is necessary to ensure that the output offset is not excessive ($V_o = V_{DI}/\beta$). This can be accomplished by having a large β for zero frequency, which is reduced at signal frequency. In Fig. 6.37, at zero frequency $\beta = \frac{1}{2}$, while at high frequency $\beta_1 = 1/1000$. This ensures that the offset is always small.

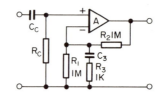

Fig. 6.37. High gain capacitor-coupled amplifier.

$$
\begin{aligned}
\beta &= \frac{\dfrac{R_1(R_3 + 1/sC_3)}{R_1 + R_3 + 1/sC_3}}{R_2 + \dfrac{R_1(R_3 + 1/sC_3)}{R_1 + R_3 + 1/sC_3}}, \\[2mm]
&= \frac{R_1}{R_1 + R_2} \cdot \frac{1 + sC_3 R_3}{1 + \dfrac{R_1 R_2 + R_2 R_3 + R_3 R_1}{R_1 + R_2} sC_3} \\[2mm]
&\doteqdot \frac{R_1}{R_1 + R_2} \cdot \frac{1 + sC_3 R_3}{1 + \dfrac{R_1 R_2}{R_1 + R_2} sC_3},
\end{aligned}
\tag{6.25}
$$

if $R_3 \ll R_1 \cdot R_2$.

The low-frequency bandwidth limit is determined by the time constant $R_3 C_3$. If R_3 is 1 kΩ, as in Fig. 6.37, and the low-frequency bandwidth is 10 Hz,

$$C_3 = \frac{1}{2\pi f R_3} = \frac{1}{2\pi \times 10 \times 10^3} = 15.9 \ \mu F.$$

The low-frequency breakpoint is given by

$$f = \frac{1}{2\pi C_3 \dfrac{R_1 R_2}{R_1 + R_2}} = 0.02 \ Hz.$$

If the breakpoint for the input coupling network is also at this frequency, the low-frequency corner of the β network is eliminated and the asymptote rises uniformly, as in Fig. 6.38b. To balance the voltages produced by the input bias currents,

$$R_c = R_1 R_2 / (R_1 + R_2) = 0.5 \ M\Omega.$$

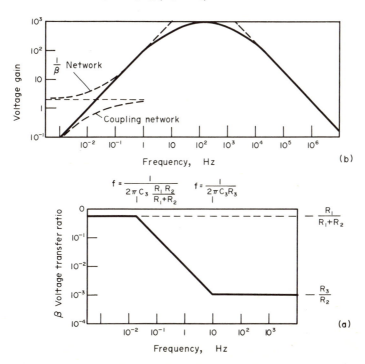

Fig. 6.38. (a) Asymptotic approximation of the β network frequency response. (b) Gain characteristic for the high-gain capacitor-coupled amplifier.

The required coupling capacitor,

$$C_c = \frac{1}{2\pi f R_c} = 15.9 \ \mu\text{F}.$$

For such a large value, an electrolytic capacitor is convenient. The necessary polarizing voltage is produced by the bias currents which, for *npn* transistors, ensure that the inputs are negative with respect to earth.

6.3.9. Selective amplifier using series–parallel feedback

By using a network such as the parallel "T" of Fig. 6.25 as the feedback element, an amplifier with the inverse response is obtained. The selective amplifier shown in Fig. 6.39 has an extremely narrow bandwidth. The closed-loop gain,

$$G = \frac{A}{1+A\beta} = \frac{A}{1+\dfrac{A}{1+4j/y}},$$

$$= \frac{A(y+4j)}{(A+1)y+4j}, \quad \text{where } y = \frac{\omega}{\omega_0} - \frac{\omega_0}{\omega}. \tag{6.26}$$

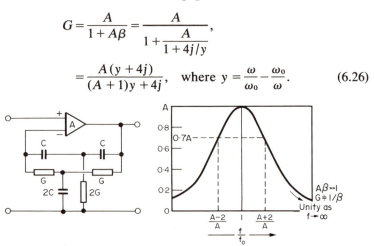

Fig. 6.39. (a) Selective amplifier using a parallel "T" network in series–parallel feedback connection, and (b) its frequency response. Maximum gain is A when $\beta = 0$ and minimum when $\beta = 1$.

When $\omega = G/C$, $y = 0$ and $G = A$, i.e. the gain at the centre frequency is A, and falls to zero when y is large. The bandwidth is found from the value of y when G falls to $G_{(max)}/\sqrt{2}$, or

$$\frac{A(y_1+4j)}{(A+1)y_1+4j} = \frac{A}{\sqrt{2}}.$$

Taking the modulus,

$$\frac{A^2(y_1^2 + 16)}{(A + 1)^2 y_1^2 + 16} = \frac{A^2}{2}.$$

From which,

$$y_1 = \sqrt{\frac{16}{A^2 + 4A - 1}} \doteq \pm\frac{4}{A}.$$

For narrow-bandwidth systems,

$$y_1 = \frac{\omega_1}{\omega_0} - \frac{\omega_0}{\omega_1} = \frac{2(\omega_1 - \omega_0)}{\omega_0},$$

so,

$$y_1 \doteq \frac{\text{Bandwidth}}{\text{Centre frequency}} = \frac{1}{Q}.$$

With $A = 10^5$, the selective amplifier Q is $A/4 = 25,000$, and for a centre frequency of 1 kHz, the bandwidth is $f_o/Q = 0.04$ Hz.

6.4. Applications of parallel–series feedback

6.4.1. Common base amplifier

The common base connection of Fig. 6.3b forms the simplest type of current amplifier. Its application is usually limited to current source operation, where an input current is defined, equal to the output current. Because of the high output resistance of the parallel–series feedback, and hence of the common base connection, an output current largely independent of external load conditions is obtained. In Fig. 6.40, a direct current sink of 2 mA is drawn.

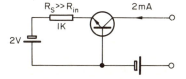

Fig. 6.40. A 2-mA current sink using a common base transistor. A current source could be formed with a *pnp* transistor.

Provided that the external resistance is not excessively large, the input resistance to the emitter of the transistor is about 20 Ω, and the 2-V supply with the 1-kΩ resistor defines a current of 2 mA. This arrangement is similar to the current source shown in Fig. 6.13, where the input voltage is supplied from the voltage divider.

6.4.2. Transistor current amplifier

It has been shown that the common base configuration can be regarded as a parallel–series connection with unity feedback. Figure 6.41a shows a more general form of current amplifier which has current gain equal to $(R_1 + R_2)/R_1$, i.e. the reciprocal of the current feedback factor. A more practical arrangement is shown in Fig. 6.41b, where the amplifier is set up to have a current gain of 10, and

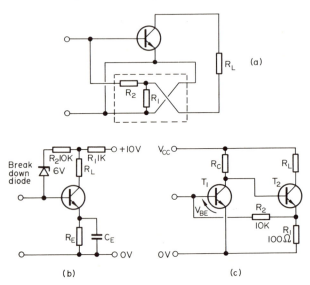

Fig. 6.41. Current amplifier connections. (a) Basic amplifier with parallel–series feedback. (b) Practical form with a gain of 11. (c) Two-stage amplifier with a current gain $(R_1 + R_2)/R_1 = 101$.

the break-down diode ensures that the collector is kept positive with respect to the base. If the supply voltage is 10 V and the diode break-down voltage is 6 V, the remaining 4 V is shared between R_1, R_E and V_{BE}. As the latter can be assumed to be 0.6 V, if R_1 and R_E

are both 1 kΩ, the voltage across these resistors will be 1.7 V. The emitter current is then 1.7 mA, if base current is neglected. The emitter resistor is bypassed for signal currents, thereby eliminating series–series feedback.

Two-stage current amplifier

An amplifier using two transistors is shown in Fig. 6.41c, where a fraction of the output transistor emitter current is fed back to the base of T_1. Again, the ratio of current in the load resistor to input current is determined by the ratio $(R_1 + R_2)/R_1$. This arrangement is not exactly of standard current amplifier form, as it is the emitter current which is controlled and not the collector current directly.

System biasing. The connection is self-adjusting as the direct voltage across R_1 is principally the base–emitter voltage of T_1. If R_1 is 100 Ω, the emitter current will be 6 mA. Likewise, the collector of T_1 will be at approximately 1.2 V, and the voltage across R_C will be $V_{CC} - 1.2$ V. The collector current for this transistor can be set by R_C, i.e. for $V_{CC} = 10$ V the collector current will be approximately 1 mA for $R_C = 8.2$ kΩ.

6.4.3. Operational amplifier current amplifiers

The general form of an operational current amplifier is shown in Fig. 6.42a where the current feedback factor is $\beta = R_1/(R_1 + R_2)$ and the closed-loop current gain is $1/\beta$. Figure 6.42b shows the feedback connection which follows the standard form of Fig. 6.2b. The current fed back is $-\beta i_o$, the negative sign arising from the convention that current flowing into a device is positive. The current

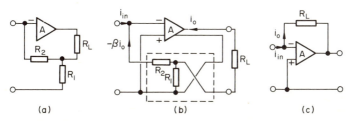

Fig. 6.42. Operational current amplifier. (a) Basic system, $\beta = R_1/(R_1 + R_2)$. (b) Standard form. (c) Unity gain current amplifier, $\beta = 1$.

flowing into the amplifier is $i_{in} - \beta i_o$. Therefore

$$i_o = A_i(i_{in} - \beta i_o) = \frac{A_i}{1 + A_i\beta} i_{in},$$

where A_i is the current gain of the amplifier and β is the current division ratio. The overall current gain of the feedback system is thus

$$G_i = \frac{i_o}{i_{in}} = \frac{A_i}{1 + A_i\beta}.$$

Note that the signs for the amplifier are for the voltage convention; a current entering the voltage *inverting* input is *not* inverted. If β is unity, all the output current is fed back and the system is as in Fig. 6.42c.

6.5. Examples of parallel–parallel feedback

As discussed in § 6.3(c), this form of feedback provides an output voltage related to the input current by the transfer impedance Z_T. This is so whether the amplifier is a current or a voltage-operated device. Figure 6.43a is an example of the latter case. If the current flowing into the amplifier is negligible, the input current,

$$i_{in} = \frac{v_{in} - v_o}{Z_F} = \frac{-v_o\left(\frac{1}{A} + 1\right)}{Z_F}, \tag{6.27}$$

since $v_o = -Av_{in}$.

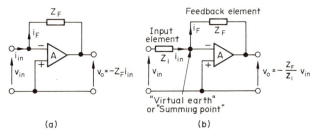

(a)   (b)

Fig. 6.43. (a) Basic parallel–parallel amplifier connection and (b) as an inverting voltage amplifier.

$$Z_T = \frac{v_o}{i_{in}} = \frac{-Z_F}{1 + \dfrac{1}{A}} \div -Z_F\left(1 - \frac{1}{A}\right),$$ (6.28)

where $1/A$ is an error term. For an amplifier having gain $A = 10^5$, the error is 0.001 per cent. The negative sign in eqn. (6.28) indicates that for a positive input current, a negative output voltage is obtained. If Z_F is a 1 MΩ resistor, a voltage equal to 1 M$\Omega \times i_{in}$ will be present at the output, i.e. for $i_{in} = 1\ \mu A$, $v_o = -1$ V.

Input resistance

Rearranging the current expression, eqn. (6.27),

$$i_{in} = \frac{v_{in} - v_o}{Z_F} = \frac{v_{in}(1 + A)}{Z_F},$$

or,

$$R_{in} = \frac{v_{in}}{i_{in}} = \frac{Z_F}{1 + A}.$$ (6.29)

If the previous values are inserted $R_{in} = 10\ \Omega$. Note that if the feedback element is a capacitor, $Z_F = 1/sC_F$ and a capacitance $C_{in} = (1 + A)C_F$ appears across the input terminals.

The most important form of parallel–parallel feedback is when the input current i_{in} is defined by an input element Z_1 as in Fig. 6.43b.

Virtual earth

Because of the low input impedance at the amplifier input, it is referred to as a *virtual earth* although there is, of course, no direct path to ground. In Fig. 6.43b, because of the virtual earth,

$$i_{in} = \frac{v_{in}}{Z_1} = -\frac{v_o}{Z_F}, \quad \text{from eqn. (6.28),}$$

whence,

$$G = \frac{v_o}{v_{in}} = -\frac{Z_F}{Z_1}.$$ (6.30)

The virtual earth is also called the *summing point*, as a number of currents can be added at the amplifier input as in Fig. 6.44. Because

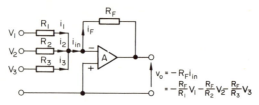

Fig. 6.44. Summing amplifier.

of the low impedance at this point, the input currents are independent. For this arrangement,

$$v_o = -\frac{Z_F}{Z_1} v_1 - \frac{Z_F}{Z_2} v_2 - \frac{Z_F}{Z_3} v_3. \qquad (6.31)$$

6.5.1. Performance of the parallel–parallel voltage amplifier

The voltage at the summing point is, from Fig. 6.45, $\alpha v_{in} + \beta v_o$,
where the feed-forward fraction

$$\alpha = \frac{R_2}{R_1 + R_2}, \qquad (6.32)$$

and the feed-back fraction,

$$\beta = \frac{R_1}{R_1 + R_2}. \qquad (6.33)$$

The output voltage,

$$v_o = -(\alpha v_{in} + \beta v_o)A = -\frac{\alpha A}{1 + A\beta} v_{in},$$

or,

$$G = \frac{v_o}{v_{in}} = -\frac{\alpha}{\beta} \left(\frac{1}{1 + \dfrac{1}{A\beta}} \right). \qquad (6.34)$$

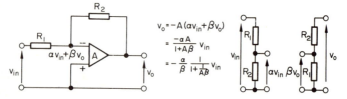

Fig. 6.45. Analysis of the parallel–parallel voltage amplifier.

Referring to Fig. 6.45, and from eqns. (6.32) and (6.33),

$$\frac{\alpha}{\beta} = \frac{R_2}{R_1}.$$

However, for multiple elements, as in Fig. 6.44, the values of α and β are modified. For input 1, α_1 is the voltage division ratio formed by R_1 and the resistance of R_2, R_3 and R_F in parallel. The feedback fraction β is the same for all the inputs and is made up of R_F and all the input elements in parallel, i.e.

$$\beta = \frac{\dfrac{R_1 R_2 R_3}{R_1 R_2 + R_2 R_3 + R_3 R_1}}{R_F + \dfrac{R_1 R_2 R_3}{R_1 R_2 + R_2 R_3 + R_3 R_1}}.$$

Error term

Using the approximate binomial expansion of eqn. (6.22), from eqn. (6.34),

$$G = -\frac{\alpha}{\beta}\left(1 - \frac{1}{A\beta}\right),$$

where $1/A\beta$ is the error term. As in the series–parallel feedback case, the precision of operation is determined by the loop gain $A\beta$. For $A = 10^5$ and $\beta = \frac{1}{2}$ ($R_1 = R_2$ in Fig. 6.45), the loop gain is 0.5×10^5,

$$G = -1(1 - 2 \times 10^{-5}),$$

and the error is 0.002 per cent. If in Fig. 6.44 all the resistors are equal, $\beta = \frac{1}{4}$ and the error is increased to 0.004 per cent.

Frequency response

As the error term for the inverting amplifier is the same as that for the series–parallel system, the same method can be used to determine the closed-loop frequency response (see Fig. 6.32). However, for a unity gain inverter $\beta = \frac{1}{2}$, not unity as for the voltage follower, so in consequence will have only half the bandwidth. The closed-loop response for a range of gains is shown in Fig. 6.46. The voltage gain, as given on the vertical axis, is no longer the closed-loop gain since it represents $1/\beta$ and not α/β.

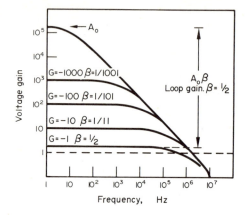

Fig. 6.46. Gain–frequency characteristic for an inverting amplifier, $G = \alpha/\beta$. The closed-loop bandwidth is the frequency at which $A = 1/\beta$.

6.5.2. Functional operations[40-42]

Operational amplifiers derive their name from the mathematical operations they can perform, the basic ones being summation, integration and differentiation.

Integration

If the feedback element is a capacitor and the input element a resistor,

$$Z_F = 1/sC \quad \text{and} \quad Z_1 = R.$$

From eqn. (6.30),

$$v_o(s) = -\frac{Z_F}{Z_1} v_{in}(s) = -\frac{1}{sCR} v_{in}(s).$$

The inverse transformation gives the output voltage as a function of time,

$$v_o(t) = -\frac{1}{CR} \int_0^t v_{in} \, dt - v_1, \tag{6.35}$$

where v_1 is the initial voltage on the capacitor. Substituting $s = j\omega$ yields the frequency response of the integrator.

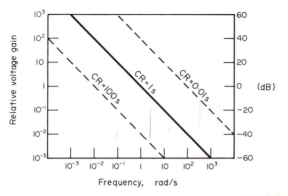

Fig. 6.47. Ideal integrator responses for three different time constants. The integrator gain, $k = 1/CR$, is equal to the radian frequency at which the response crosses the unity gain line.

$$\frac{v_o(j\omega)}{v_{in}(j\omega)} = -\frac{1}{j\omega CR} = -\frac{k}{j\omega}. \qquad (6.36)$$

The magnitude of this expression is represented by a straight line passing through the unity gain axis at $\omega = 1/CR$, as in Fig. 6.47. The integrator has a voltage gain which is inversely proportional to frequency. The term "integrator gain", k, is reserved for the coefficient of the integral in eqn. (6.35), and is the reciprocal of the CR time constant. It represents the output voltage for a 1-V step input applied for unit time. If CR is 1 second the gain is unity, i.e. a 1-V step input produces -1 V at the output after 1 second. Figure 6.48 shows that the output voltage falls by an amount equal to the input voltage after an interval of one time constant.

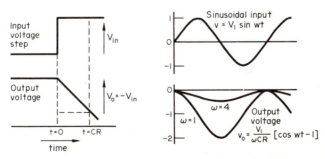

Fig. 6.48. Response of an integrator to a step function and a sinewave input.

Integrator performance

The integrator loop gain is found by adding the logarithmic responses of the amplifier and β network, as in Fig. 6.49a. It is apparent that the loop gain falls at low frequency, which is to be expected because of the capacitor in the feedback path. The

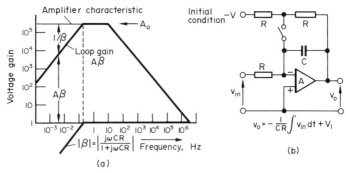

Fig. 6.49. (a) Integrator loop-gain construction using straight-line approximations. $CR = 1$ s. (b) Integrator schematic diagram with initial condition network.

integrator is "zero frequency unstable" and in many applications will require some means of discharging the capacitor, or of charging it to some specified initial value. This can be accomplished using the simple method of Fig. 6.49b.

Integrator drift

The amplifier bias current is supplied from the charge on the capacitor. This will cause the output voltage to change, even though there is no input signal. If $C = 1\ \mu\text{F}$, and the bias current, i_A, is 10^{-7} A, since $Q = CV$, the rate of change of output voltage is

$$\frac{\mathrm{d}v_o}{\mathrm{d}t} = \frac{i_A}{C} = \frac{10^{-7}}{10^{-6}} = 0.1\ \text{V/s}.$$

For long-term integration, or for storing a voltage on the capacitor, an amplifier with low input current is desirable, e.g. a FET input type. Another current component is that drawn by the input resistance and input resistor. In Fig. 6.50, the voltage v_A is the offset voltage together with the voltage, v_o/A, necessary to maintain the output. This, applied across R_A and R_1 in parallel, will draw a

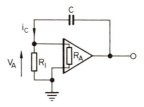

Fig. 6.50. Integrator capacitor current associated with the input resistances.

current which again is supplied by the capacitor. If the offset voltage is 5 mV, the amplifier input resistance is 100 kΩ and R_1 is also 100 kΩ, a capacitor current will flow,

$$i_C = \frac{V_{DI}}{R_A R_1/(R_A + R_1)} = \frac{5 \text{ mV}}{50 \text{ k}\Omega} = 10^{-7} \text{ A.}$$

The use of automatic zero correction in an amplifier improves its performance by removing the bias current from the capacitor path, reducing the offset and increasing the amplifier gain.

Integrator performance at low frequency

The integrator response has been shown to be $v_o/v_{in} = -1/sCR$. Since, from Fig. 6.51a,

$$\alpha = \frac{1}{1 + sCR} \quad \text{and} \quad \beta = \frac{sCR}{1 + sCR},$$

it follows that,

$$\frac{v_o}{v_{in}} = -\left[\frac{1}{1 + sCR} \times \frac{1 + sCR}{sCR} \right] = -\frac{\alpha}{\beta}.$$

Also shown in Fig. 6.51a are the asymptotic frequency responses of $|\alpha|$ and $|\beta|$. Because they are plotted on logarithmic axes, the division α/β implies the subtraction of their relevant ordinates, and results in the closed-loop curve drawn in Fig. 6.51b. This has been superposed on the frequency response of the amplifier itself.

For the closed-loop response $G = A/(1 + A\beta) \doteqdot 1/\beta$. The loop gain characteristic $A\beta$ is therefore obtained by dividing the amplifier gain A by the closed-loop gain $1/\beta$, i.e. by subtracting ordinates, as before. The resulting loop-gain response is also shown in Fig. 6.51b.

The low-frequency gain limitation is now apparent. The frequency

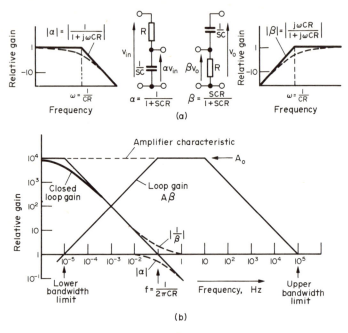

Fig. 6.51. Construction of closed-loop integrator characteristic. The integrator gain is 0.628.

at which $A\beta = 1$, where the ideal integrator line meets the amplifier curve, can be considered as the low-frequency bandwidth limit. The upper bandwidth limit is that of the amplifier itself, so in this case the bandwidth is ten decades, from 10^{-5} to 10^{5} Hz. The low-frequency performance can be improved by increasing A_o, the amplifier gain. Alternatively, it may be improved by reducing the integrator gain k. However, it is often required that integrator gain be high and a poor low-frequency response results.

Error in the integrator time response

An alternative approach is to look at the error in the integrator response to a step input. From eqn. (6.34),

$$v_o = \frac{-\alpha A_o}{1 + A_o \beta} v_{\text{in}}.$$

Substituting for α and β,

$$v_o(s) = \frac{-\dfrac{A_o}{1+sCR}}{1+\dfrac{sCRA_o}{1+sCR}} v_{in}(s).$$

From Appendix B, for a step input $v_{in}(s) = V_1/s$, so

$$v_o(s) = \frac{-A_o}{1+sCR(1+A_o)} \cdot \frac{V_1}{s}.$$

Therefore,

$$v_o(t) = -V_1 A_o\left[1 - \exp\left(\frac{-t}{CR(1+A_o)}\right)\right]. \qquad (6.37)$$

Expanding the exponential,

$$v_o(t) = -V_1 A_o\left[1 - 1 + \frac{t}{CR(1+A_o)} - \frac{t^2}{2[CR(1+A_o)]^2} + - \right]$$

$$= \frac{-V_1 A_o t}{CR(1+A_o)}\left[1 - \frac{t}{2[CR(1+A_o)]} + - \right] \qquad (6.38)$$

From eqn. (6.35), with no initial conditions, $v_o(t) = -V_1 t/CR$. Thus, two errors are apparent, a constant error $A_o/(1+A_o)$, which is

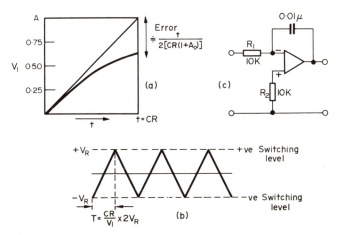

Fig. 6.52. (a) Integrator time-dependent error. (b) Voltage-to-frequency converter waveform. (c) Integrator with 10^{-4} s time constant and gain of 10^4.

negligible for large gains, and an error which increases with time. This latter error can have serious effects if an integrator with a small time constant is required to integrate over a long time interval, as illustrated in Fig. 6.52a.

Example

The triangular waveform of Fig. 6.52b is formed by an integrator which has its input voltage reversed when the output reaches a specified upper and lower level, and the frequency of the waveform is proportional to the input voltage. This system forms the basis for a voltage-to-frequency converter. The upper frequency is determined by the time constant CR, let this be 10^{-4} s, and when the input voltage is small let the maximum period be 1 second. It is required that the error should be no greater than 1% for this condition. Thus,

$$\frac{t}{2[CR(1 + A_0)]} \leqslant \frac{1}{100},$$

or

$$A_o + 1 \geqslant \frac{100}{2 \times 10^{-4}} = 0.5 \times 10^6.$$

This is difficult to meet with an ordinary operational amplifier, but is readily obtained using an automatic offset controlled type (see § 6.9).

Passive integrator components

Referring to Fig. 6.52c, the capacitor should be as large as possible to reduce the effects of bias and leakage currents, and the resistor should be large enough to limit the current to that which can be supplied by the amplifier. A safe value is about $10\,\text{k}\Omega$, although smaller values can be used in some applications. The purpose of R_2 is to balance the voltages produced by the bias current.

6.5.3. Difference integrator

The arrangement of Fig. 6.53 can be analysed by the use of superposition, in which each input is considered separately and the results then combined. For input 1 a signal V_1 is integrated, so, as before,

$$v_{o1} = -\frac{\alpha_1}{\beta} = -\frac{v_1}{sCR}.$$

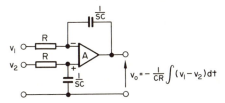

Fig. 6.53. Difference integrator.

Input 2, the non-inverting input, makes a series–parallel connection and has the form shown in Fig. 6.31 for which

$$\frac{v_{o2}}{v_{in}} \doteq \frac{1}{\beta}. \tag{6.23}$$

In this case, however, $v_{in2} = \alpha_2 v_2$ where the feed-forward factor of input 2 is

$$\alpha_2 = \frac{1}{1 + sCR}.$$

Thus,

$$v_{o2} = \frac{\alpha_2}{\beta} v_2.$$

Since $\beta = sCR/(1 + sCR)$,

$$v_{o2} = \left(\frac{1}{1 + sCR} \times \frac{1 + sCR}{sCR}\right) v_2 = \frac{v_2}{sCR}.$$

Combining the two outputs,

$$v_o(s) = v_{o1} + v_{o2} = -\frac{1}{sCR}(v_1 - v_2),$$

$$v_o(t) = -\frac{1}{CR} \int (v_1 - v_2) dt, \tag{6.39}$$

and the arrangement functions as a difference integrator.

    Error term. Such a treatment does not yield the error term and if this is required to be known a slightly different approach is necessary. The voltage at the inverting input is $\alpha_1 v_1 + \beta v_o$ and at the non-inverting input it is $\alpha_2 v_2$. Thus the differential input voltage $v_A = \alpha_1 v_1 + \beta v_o - \alpha_2 v_2$, i.e.

$$v_A = \frac{v_1}{1 + sCR} + \frac{v_o sCR}{1 + sCR} - \frac{v_2}{1 + sCR} = \frac{v_o}{A},$$

$$v_o\left[\frac{1}{A} - \frac{sCR}{1 + sCR}\right] = \frac{v_1 - v_2}{1 + sCR},$$

$$- v_o sCR = v_1 - v_2 - \frac{v_o(1 + sCR)}{A},$$

$$v_o = -\frac{1}{sCR}\left[(v_1 - v_2) + \frac{v_o}{A}(1 + sCR)\right],$$

and the error term is apparent.

6.5.4. Double integrator

The feedback network in Fig. 6.54a supplies a feedback current, $-i_f$, to the summing point of the amplifier. This current is

$$-i_f = \frac{(sC)^2 R}{2(1 + sCR)}v_o,$$

and can be found by analysis of Fig. 6.54b.

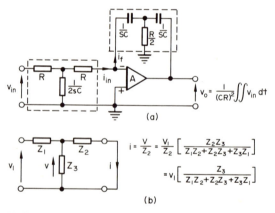

(a)

(b)

Fig. 6.54. Double integrator. The overall transfer function is the transfer impedance v_o/i_F of the feedback network, divided by the transfer impedance v_{in}/i_{in} of the feed-forward network.

Similarly,

$$i_{in} = \frac{1}{2R(1 + sCR)}\,v_{in}.$$

At the summing point $i_{in} = i_f$, assuming the amplifier input current is negligible, and

$$\frac{v_{in}}{2R(1+sCR)} = \frac{-(sC)^2 R v_o}{2(1+sCR)},$$

from which,

$$\frac{v_o}{v_{in}} = -\frac{1}{(sCR)^2}.$$

The network therefore performs double integration.

6.5.5. Differentiation

If, as in Fig. 6.55a, the input element to a parallel–parallel system is a capacitor, and the feedback element is a resistor,

$$i_{in} = sCv_{in} \quad \text{and} \quad i_f = -v_o/R.$$

Equating currents as before,

$$\frac{v_o(s)}{v_{in}(s)} = -sCR. \tag{6.40}$$

The time response is,

$$v_o(t) = -CR\frac{d}{dt}v_{in}(t),$$

and the system performs the function of differentiation. The frequency response is obtained by substituting $j\omega$ for s, in eqn. (6.40),

$$\frac{v_o(j\omega)}{v_{in}(j\omega)} = -j\omega CR.$$

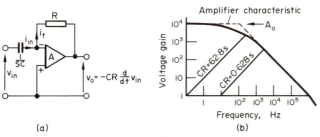

(a)   (b)

Fig. 6.55. Operational amplifier differentiator. (a) Schematic diagram. (b) The differentiator characteristic. The amplifier gain A_o controls the high frequency range of the response.

This indicates a voltage gain which is proportional to frequency, a 90° phase lead due to the j term, and signal inversion. The gain–frequency response is shown in Fig. 6.55b with the high-frequency limit set by the amplifier characteristic.

An important aspect of this limitation is seen if a curve is drawn for the $A\beta$ loop gain, as in Fig. 6.56. In this case, the feed-forward and feedback fractions are,

$$\alpha = \frac{sCR}{1 + sCR} \quad \text{and} \quad \beta = \frac{1}{1 + sCR}.$$

Phase lag is introduced by the amplifier at its breakpoint, which adds to that of the β network. (The β network of an integrator provides

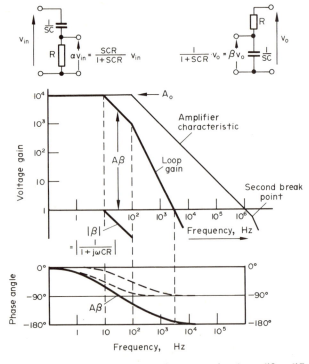

Fig. 6.56. Loop-gain frequency response of an operational amplifier differentiator using straight-line approximation. Note that the differentiator is zero-frequency stable, the resistive feedback ensuring that the loop gain is finite at low frequency.

phase advance.) The additional lag can affect the stability of the system.

For a closed-loop system the gain can be written as

$$G = \frac{A}{1 + A\beta},$$

which equals infinity for $A\beta = -1$. Thus, the condition for instability is that $|A\beta| = 1$ and $\angle A\beta = -180°$. Referring to Fig. 6.56, if the phase shift becomes $-180°$ before the magnitude of the loop gain has fallen to unity, the amplifier will oscillate, i.e. the negative feedback will have become positive. For the curves drawn, the phase angle has not quite reached $-180°$ when $|A\beta|$ is unity so the system represented is just stable. However, the *phase margin* ($180° - \angle A\beta$ when $|A\beta|$ is unity) is sufficiently small to indicate the possibility of instability occurring when any additional small phase shift is introduced at a frequency below that for which $|A\beta| > 1$. Two points should here be mentioned. Firstly, with many operational amplifiers a second breakpoint exists and an extra 45° of lag is introduced at the frequency of this breakpoint. Usually, however, this occurs at a frequency which is sufficiently high for $|A\beta|$ to be already less than unity. Secondly, shunt capacitance at the summing point of an operational amplifier has the same destabilizing effect as has been discussed for the differentiator.

Stabilization of the differentiator

A small resistor in series with the capacitor has the effect of compensating for the phase lag of the β network at high frequency where, however, the system no longer behaves as a pure differentiator. In Fig. 6.57 the high-frequency gain is 100.

$$\alpha = \frac{sCR}{1 + sC(R_1 + R)} \quad \text{and} \quad \beta = \frac{1 + sCR_1}{1 + sC(R_1 + R)}.$$

Differentiator limitations

   (a) The input capacitor has a destabilizing effect.
   (b) As indicated in Fig. 6.55, the gain increases with frequency. In consequence, high-frequency noise, which is often present in electronic systems, is accentuated.
   (c) The capacitor can demand a large charging current for input

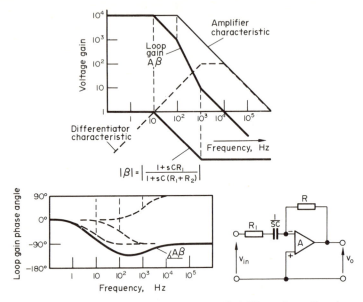

$$|\beta| = \left|\frac{1+sCR_1}{1+sC(R_1+R_2)}\right|$$

Fig. 6.57. Loop-gain frequency response for a modified differentiator. R_1 reduces the maximum phase angle as well as the range of operation.

waveforms with large dV/dt. For the input waveform shown in Fig. 6.58a, and the differentiator of Fig. 6.58b, the input current is

$$i = C\frac{dv}{dt} = 2 \times 10^4 \times 10^{-6} = 20\,\text{mA}.$$

This could be too large a current to be supplied from an operational amplifier.

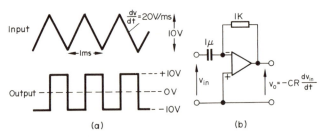

(a)   (b)

Fig. 6.58. Input and output waveforms for a differentiator with a gain of 10^3. Because of output current limitations, more satisfactory component values would be $C = 0.1\,\mu\text{F}$ and $R = 10\,\text{k}\Omega$.

DESIGN EXAMPLE 6.2

Required, a differentiator to provide an output of 10 V, for an input signal having a rate of change of 5 V/ms.

A sine wave of peak amplitude E changes at a rate of

$$\frac{d}{dt} E \sin \omega t = \omega E \cos \omega t,$$

which has a maximum value of ωE. For $\omega E = 5$ V/ms, and $E = 10$ V,

$$\omega = 500 \text{ rad/s}, \quad \text{and} \quad f = 79.6 \text{ Hz}.$$

Time constant (differentiator gain)

$$v_0 = - CR\frac{dv_{in}}{dt}.$$

Substituting values,

$$CR = \frac{10 \text{ V}}{5 \text{ V/ms}} = 0.2 \times 10^{-2} \text{ s}.$$

Feedback resistor. If R is $10 \text{ k}\Omega$, and the maximum output

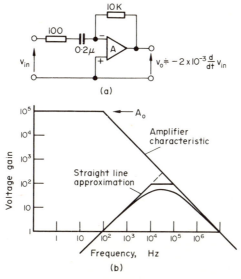

Fig. 6.59. Schematic diagram and frequency response of an approximate differentiator.

voltage is 10 V, the output current (and also the input current) is limited to 1 mA, which is a reasonable value.

Capacitor

$$C = \frac{0.2 \times 10^{-2}}{10^4} = 0.2 \; \mu\text{F}.$$

The voltage gain at $\omega = 1$ rad/s is is $CR = 2 \times 10^{-3}$, and unity voltage gain is at 79.6 Hz, where $\omega CR = 1$.

Stabilizing resistor. A 100-Ω resistor in series with the input capacitor has the effect of limiting the gain to 100, as shown in Fig. 6.59b. This ensures stability and reduces the level of output noise.

6.6.   Example of series–series feedback

This form of feedback is described in § 6.2(d), where it is shown that the feedback element defines the transfer admittance of a network, i.e. the output current divided by the input voltage.

A precision current sink, which is an extension of the system of Fig. 6.4b, is shown in Fig. 6.60a. The output follower is of the type shown in Fig. 6.21b, and is used because it draws no current from the operational amplifier. Consequently, all the current in R_1 is derived from i_o, the sink current.

Performance can be assessed by assuming a high-voltage gain for

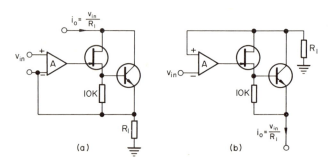

Fig. 6.60. (a) Current sink provided by series–series feedback. The load is connected between the positive voltage supply and the sink, and v_{in} must be positive. (b) Current source arrangement. The load is connected between the transistor emitter and the negative supply.

A, which requires that the voltage at the inverting input be close to that at the non-inverting input. The output voltage,

$$v_R = (v_{in} - v_R)A = \frac{v_{in}}{1 + 1/A}.$$

The output current,

$$i_0 = \frac{v_R}{R_1} = \frac{v_{in}}{R_1(1 + 1/A)} \doteqdot \frac{v_{in}}{R_1}.$$

Thus, the transfer conductance $i_o/v_{in} = 1/R_1$.

A system which functions as a *current source* is drawn in Fig. 6.60b. In this example R_1, being joined to the drain and collector of the output stage, provides a feedback voltage which is inverted with respect to the operational amplifier output voltage. To obtain the over-all signal inversion necessary for negative feedback operation, the feedback is taken to the non-inverting input.

Assuming that the two amplifier inputs follow each other closely,

$$v_{in} = R_1 i_o \quad \text{or,} \quad i_o = \frac{v_{in}}{R_1}.$$

6.7.   Instrumentation using feedback amplifiers

6.7.1.   Millivoltmeter

A high input impedance voltmeter can be formed using the series–series connection of Fig. 6.60.

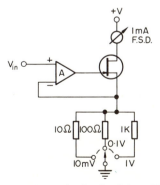

Fig. 6.61. Application of series–series feedback for millivoltmeter operation.

A direct voltage millivoltmeter, which uses a 1-mA full-scale moving-coil meter as the indicator, is shown in Fig. 6.61.

6.7.2. Transducer amplifier

In Fig. 6.62, R represents a transducer such as a strain gauge, and R_1 is a resistance of equivalent value, $(R = R_1 + \Delta R)$. Since the system is a parallel–parallel feedback connection,

$$v_o = -\frac{R_2}{R}V + \frac{R_2}{R_1}V,$$

$$= -\left[\frac{1}{R_1 + \Delta R} - \frac{1}{R_1}\right]R_2V,$$

$$= -\left[\frac{R_1 - R_1 - \Delta R}{(R_1 + \Delta R)R_1}\right]R_2V,$$

$$= \frac{\Delta R/R_1}{(1 + \Delta R/R_1)} \cdot \frac{R_2}{R_1}V.$$

Thus,

$$v_o \doteqdot \Delta R/R_1 \cdot \frac{R_2}{R_1}V,$$

where ΔR is much smaller than R_1. The change in resistance of R is proportional to the change in output voltage.

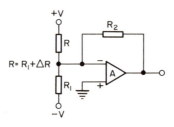

+V

R_2

$R = R_1 + \Delta R$

R

R_1

A

−V

Fig. 6.62. Transducer amplifier.

Resistor values.   The resistor R_2 must not be smaller than $10\,\text{k}\Omega$, or it could overload the amplifier output. Normally R_2 should not be greater than $1\,\text{M}\Omega$, as larger values increase the sensitivity to input current variations.

6.7.3. Difference amplifier

The parallel–parallel feedback connection can utilize the amplifier non-inverting input for introducing a second input signal, as in Fig. 6.63a. The output voltage can then be regarded as the sum of two

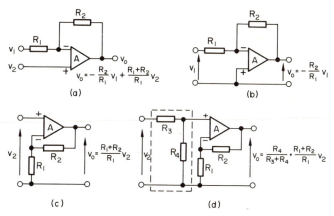

Fig. 6.63. (a) The basic difference amplifier in (b) parallel–parallel operation with v_2 zero, and (c) series–parallel operation with v_1 zero. (d) Modification of series–parallel connection by an input network, $\alpha' = R_4/(R_3 + R_4)$.

outputs, one from a parallel–parallel system and the other from a series–parallel system, i.e.

$$v_o = -\frac{R_2}{R_1}v_1 + \frac{R_1 + R_2}{R_1}v_2,$$

where the individual components are determined as in Fig. 6.63 (b) and (c). If the series–parallel connection of Fig. 6.63c is modified by the insertion of an input attenuator network, as in Fig. 6.63d,

$$v_o = \frac{\alpha'}{\beta}v_2,$$

where,

$$\alpha' = \frac{R_4}{R_3 + R_4} \quad \text{and} \quad \beta = \frac{R_1 + R_2}{R_1}.$$

A *balanced difference amplifier* is drawn in Fig. 6.64a, in which the output is proportional to the difference of the input signals.

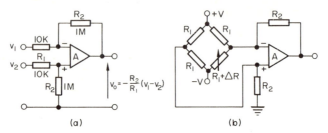

Fig. 6.64. The balanced difference amplifier, (a) with a differential gain of -100 and (b) as a bridge amplifier.

$$v_0 = -\frac{\alpha}{\beta}(v_1 - v_2) = -\frac{R_2}{R_1}(v_1 - v_2).$$

The effective resistances are the same in each input connection, thus ensuring that the bias current voltage drops are equal.

Common mode signals

The ideal difference amplifier has zero output voltage for $v_1 = v_2$, i.e. for equal voltages applied at the two inputs. Such voltages are *common mode* inputs. Generally, the common mode input is the mean of the input voltages, $(v_1 + v_2)/2$. If $v_1 = 5$ V and $v_2 = -1$ V, the common mode input is 2 V.

Differential signals

The difference of the input voltages is the *differential mode* input. Thus if again, $v_1 = 5$ V and $v_2 = -1$ V, the differential mode input is $v_1 - v_2 = 6$ V.

Common mode gain

In the system of Fig. 6.64a the common mode gain is zero, since the two gains have the same magnitude. If $R_1 = R_2$, the output would be -6 V, and would be the same if the input voltages were 9 V and 3 V.

However, the common mode gain is never exactly zero, one reason for this being inaccuracies in the matching of the resistors in the α and β networks. The common mode gain can be found by joining the inputs, and measuring the output voltage produced by the common input voltage.

The ratio

$$\frac{\text{differential gain}}{\text{common mode gain}} = \frac{G_d}{G_{\text{CM}}} = \text{CMR}, \qquad (6.41)$$

is the *common mode rejection ratio*, which is frequently greater than 10^5 (or 100 dB). The output voltage is the sum of the differential output plus the common mode output. For inputs of 30 mV and 0 V, a differential gain of 100 would produce an output of 3 V, the common mode signal being negligible. If $v_1 = 10.03$ V and $v_2 = 10$ V, the differential output would be the same. However, for a CMR of 10^5, the common code gain

$$G_{\text{CM}} = \frac{G_d}{\text{CMR}} = 10^{-3},$$

yielding a common mode output voltage of

$$10.015 \times 10^{-3} = 0.010015 \text{ V},$$

and thus introducing an error of 0.3 per cent.

6.7.4. Bridge amplifier

A disadvantage of the network of Fig. 6.62 is that the amplifier output is sensitive to changes in the voltages $+\text{V}$ and $-\text{V}$. This is not the case for the bridge amplifier of Fig. 6.64b since in such a balanced system such changes appear as common mode signals and are rejected.

The input resistors of the system are formed by the arms of the bridge and, for maximum sensitivity, the arms should be equal, i.e. the resistance of each limb should equal that of the transducer element. Normally the R_1 resistors would be greater than 1 MΩ because of matching problems with high resistance values and, additionally, bias current problems.

6.7.5. High-input impedance difference amplifiers

The arrangement of Fig. 6.65a uses two follower amplifiers which operate into a difference amplifier, and

$$v_o = -\frac{R_3 + R_4}{R_4} \cdot \frac{R_2}{R_1}(v_1 - v_2). \qquad (6.42)$$

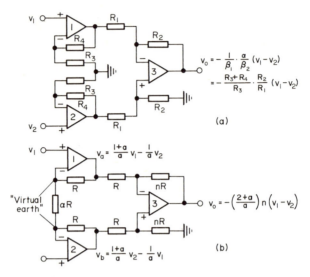

$$v_o = -\frac{1}{\beta_1} \cdot \frac{a}{\beta_2} (v_1 - v_2)$$

$$= -\frac{R_3 + R_4}{R_3} \cdot \frac{R_2}{R_1} (v_1 - v_2)$$

(a)

$$v_a = \frac{1+a}{a} v_1 - \frac{1}{a} v_2$$

$$v_o = -\left(\frac{2+a}{a}\right) n \left(v_1 - v_2\right)$$

(b)

$$v_b = \frac{1+a}{a} v_2 - \frac{1}{a} v_1$$

Fig. 6.65. High-input resistance difference amplifiers. In (b) the gain can be changed by varying resistor aR. For $a = 1$ and $n = 1$, the gain is 3.

The alternative form of Fig. 6.65b has the input amplifiers coupled by a common resistor. The output voltage of amplifier 1 is found by considering input v_1 and series–parallel operation, with the virtual earth of amplifier 2 holding the bottom end of aR at zero voltage. The common resistor aR can also be considered as an input resistor to the inverting input of amplifier 2, producing an output $-(1/a)v_2$. Thus, for amplifier 1, the output

$$v_a = \frac{1+a}{a} v_1 - \frac{1}{a} v_2,$$

and similarly for amplifier 2,

$$v_b = -\frac{1}{a} v_1 + \frac{1+a}{a} v_2.$$

Amplifier 3 functions as a difference amplifier with input voltages v_a and v_b, giving an output

$$v_o = -n\left(\frac{a+2}{a}\right)(v_1 - v_2).$$

The common mode gain of the input amplifiers is unity, which enables larger common mode signals to be handled than in the system of the previous example.

6.8 Low-input resistance amplifier

It is usually assumed that an operational amplifier has an input resistance which is sufficiently large for the current flowing into the amplifier to be neglected. An alternative situation is that the amplifier has a low-input resistance, and is operated by a current rather than a voltage input. If such an amplifier has a high performance, the required current will be so much smaller than that flowing in the external elements, that no significant errors are introduced.

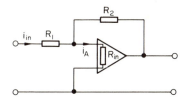

Fig. 6.66. Low-input resistance amplifier. R_{in} is less than R_1. If the internal transfer resistance is much greater than R_2, i_A will be much less than i_{in}.

In Fig. 6.66 the amplifier draws an input current i_A. For this parallel–parallel system the loop gain is

$$A\beta = A_v \frac{R_1}{R_1 + R_2},$$

where A_v is voltage gain. If R_{in}, the input resistance to the amplifier is very much less than R_1,

$$\beta \doteqdot \frac{R_{in}}{R_{in} + R_2},$$

and

$$A\beta \doteqdot A_v \frac{R_{in}}{R_{in} + R_2}.$$

Since the amplifier provides an output voltage as a function of input

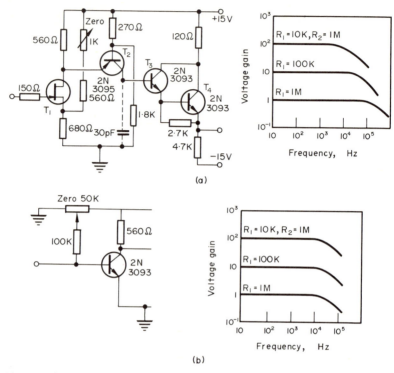

Fig. 6.67. Closed-loop responses for (a) high- and (b) low-input resistance amplifiers. The latter maintains its bandwidth with increasing gain.

current, it is convenient to consider the transfer resistance of the amplifier rather than the voltage gain.

Transfer resistance $R_T = A_v R_{in}$, and the loop gain

$$A\beta = \frac{R_T}{R_{in} + R_2} \doteq \frac{R_T}{R_2}, \quad \text{if } R_{in} \ll R_2.$$

It is apparent that the loop gain $A\beta$, in the case of a low-input resistance amplifier, is independent of the input element R_1, and is determined only by the feedback element R_2. The bandwidth of the closed-loop amplifier is a function of the feedback element and not of the β network as is the case for the high input resistance system.

In Fig. 6.67 the performances of two systems are compared, one system having a FET input and the other a bipolar transistor. It is apparent that the bandwidth of the latter remains relatively constant as the gain is varied, provided that R_1 is considerably greater than R_{in} (about $2 \, k\Omega$ in this case). A smaller value of R_2 increases the degree of feedback and extends the bandwidth.

For the low-input resistance system, the closed-loop gain,

$$G = -\frac{R_2}{R_1} \frac{1}{1 + 1/A\beta} = -\frac{R_2}{R_1} \frac{1}{1 + R_2/R_T}. \qquad (6.43)$$

With the bipolar input of Fig. 6.67b, the transfer resistance of the amplifier is made up of the current gain of that stage ($\doteqdot 50$), multiplied by the current gain of the second stage (unity), multiplied by the effective load resistance, which is the input resistance of the Darlington stage ($\doteqdot 2 \, M\Omega$). Thus, $R_T \doteqdot 50 \times 1 \times 2 \, M\Omega \doteqdot -100 \, M\Omega$.

For a feedback resistor of $R_2 = 1 \, M\Omega$, the error is R_2/R_T or 1 per cent. For $R_2 = 100 \, k\Omega$, the error is reduced to 0.1 per cent and is independent of R_1.

Integrated circuit low input resistance systems

Because of the low cost and ready availability of integrated forms of direct-coupled amplifiers, the use of discrete components is unattractive on counts of both cost and performance. However, in the design of IC operational amplifiers, emphasis is placed on achieving a high input resistance, so that it is typically a megohm or

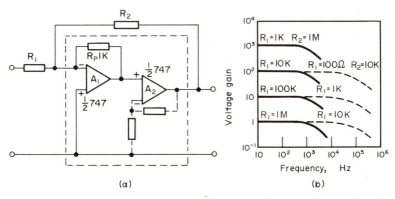

(a)   (b)

Fig. 6.68. (a) Low-input resistance amplifier. The input resistance for the parallel–parallel stage is $R_p/A_v = 0.005 \, \Omega$. (b) Gain curves for two feedback resistor values show that the bandwidth is determined by R_2.

more. To obtain a low input resistance, two amplifiers are required as in Fig. 6.68a. The first, connected in parallel–parallel, provides the low input resistance (approximately R_F/A). The second amplifier operates in series–parallel, or open loop as a non-inverting stage. In the latter case the overall transfer resistance is

$$R_T = -1\,\text{k}\Omega \times 2 \times 10^5 = -200\,\text{M}\Omega.$$

Figure 6.68b shows the closed-loop gain curves for this arrange-

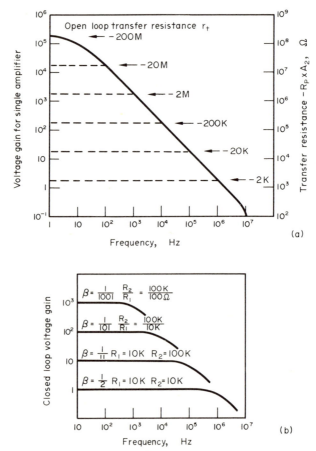

Fig. 6.69. (a) Determination of transfer resistance from the open-loop response. (b) The bandwidth of the closed-loop system is the frequency at which the feedback resistor R_2 is equal to the overall transfer resistance, $R_p A_2$.

ment. The bandwidth is determined by the value of R_2, the feedback resistor, and it is thus possible to have a range of gains with constant bandwidth. This can be found from the characteristic of Fig. 6.69a where the open-loop gain is multiplied by the transfer resistance of the first stage. This has a wide bandwidth because of the high degree of feedback, and does not modify the amplifier frequency characteristic to any great extent. The estimated bandwidth corresponds closely to the measured response.

The conventional single-stage response is given in Fig. 6.69b and shows that the bandwidth is a function of β. The bandwidth is that frequency at which $A = 1/\beta$, whereas for the low input resistance system the bandwidth is the frequency at which $R_T = R_2$. For $R_2 = 200 \, \text{k}\Omega$, the term R_2/R_T will be unity at $10^4 \, \text{Hz}$, and the bandwidth will remain constant at this value as the gain is altered by varying R_1.

6.9. Automatic zeroing

Direct-coupled amplifiers using discrete components, and many IC systems, require some method of bringing the output voltage to zero when the input voltage is zero.

It has been shown in § 6.3.8 that the output voltage, due to an input referred offset V_{DI}, is

$$v_o = \frac{V_{DI}A}{1 + A\beta} = \frac{V_{DI}}{\beta}.$$

For a standard operational amplifier V_{DI} is approximately 4 mV, and for a unity gain inverter for which $\beta = \frac{1}{2}$, the output voltage would be 8 mV. If the closed-loop gain is -100, the output voltage will be nearly 5 per cent of the 10-V full-scale output voltage. Often, provision is made for reducing the offset voltage by means of an external control, but in large systems this can be inconvenient because of access problems.

Reduction of input referred offset

If an amplifier is preceded by a zero offset amplifier, as in Fig. 6.70a, the output offset is unaltered but, for the combination, the input referred offset is the output offset divided by the total gain.

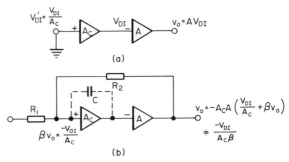

Fig. 6.70. (a) Voltage offset relationships with a zero offset pre-amplifier arrangement. In (b) high-frequency signals bypass the auxiliary amplifier through C.

Thus,

$$V'_{DI} = \frac{V_{DI} \times A}{A_c \times A} = \frac{V_{DI}}{A_c},$$

and the input offset has been reduced by the gain of the first amplifier. When this amplifier is incorporated into a feedback system, as in Fig. 6.70b, the output voltage due to the offset is $V_{DI}/A_c\beta$, and has been reduced by A_c, the gain of the auxiliary amplifier. Thus, for a gain of $A_c = 1000$, the offset output for the typical unity inverter connection will be $8 \text{ mV}/10^3 = 8 \ \mu\text{V}$. With this arrangement the output can be sufficiently close to zero, when the input is zero, to remove the necessity for a manual zero control. A suitable A_c amplifier is the *chopper* type, already mentioned in Chapter 4, which is redrawn for ease of reference in Fig. 6.71a.

An input signal is converted into a pulsating signal by the shunt switch. This is amplified by a capacitor-coupled amplifier, and synchronously rectified by the second shunt switch. Since the· amplifier can only amplify alternating signals, any offset is due to the input switch. This has had many forms, an original one making use of an electro-mechanical relay. Subsequently it has been replaced by a succession of semiconductor devices, from the junction transistor to opto-electronic choppers.

The system shown in Fig. 6.74 uses an insulated gate field effect input chopper. This gives the required isolation between the switching waveform and the input signal, although a capacitive spike is fed into the amplifier input. The synchronous rectifier is a junction FET,

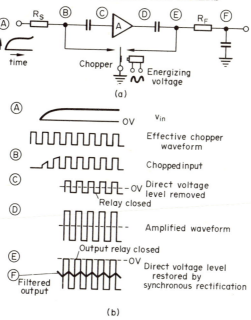

Fig. 6.71. (a) A basic chopper amplifier with (b) its relevant waveforms.

which is satisfactory for operation at the output, as this position is less sensitive than the input. As shown in Fig. 6.72, for small drain voltages the FET behaves as a variable resistor controlled by the gate voltage. The output is a pulsating unidirectional voltage, which is smoothed by an *RC* filter. Such a filter limits the bandwidth to a low value, usually considerably less than 1 Hz.

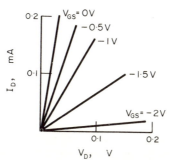

Fig. 6.72. Field effect transistor, low-voltage characteristics.

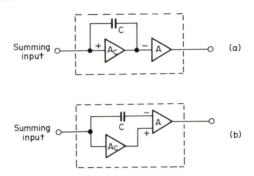

Fig. 6.73. Two feed-forward methods for high-frequency signals in chopper-stabilized systems. In (b) bias currents are isolated from the summing point.

In the system of Fig. 6.73b, high-frequency signals pass directly to the inverting input of the main amplifier. The output is a superposition of the path through the auxiliary amplifier and the non-inverting input of the main amplifier, and the direct path through the inverting input. The overall gain is therefore $A + AA_c$ or $A(1 + A_c)$, where both A and A_c vary with frequency. The advantages obtained with this increased complexity are

(a) greatly reduced offset,
(b) high gain at low frequencies and
(c) complete isolation of the summing point from the amplifier bias currents.

All of these are of significance for long-term integration. A disadvantage is that there will always be noise signals generated by the chopper amplifier. A major component of this noise is the capacitive spikes injected into the system, often through the input chopper. However, in integrator operation the system significantly reduces such noise, and for low-frequency operation the effects can be largely removed by a capacitor in parallel with the feedback resistor R_2. Nevertheless, to limit the average energy in the spikes, the chopping frequency is usually kept below 1 kHz.

DESIGN EXAMPLE 6.3
Required, an electronic integrator having a time constant of 10^{-4} s. For an integration time of 1 s, the error is to be no greater than 1 per cent of the 10 V maximum output signal.

Selection of integrating resistor and capacitor. It is desirable that the capacitor should be as large as possible, consistent with the minimum value for R. This is limited to about $10\,k\Omega$, for current reasons. Let $C = 0.01\ \mu F$ and $R = 10\,k\Omega$, as in Fig. 6.74.

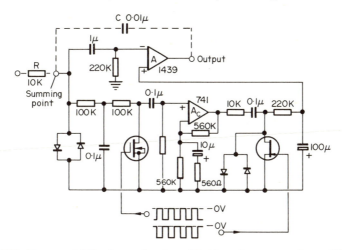

Fig. 6.74. Chopper-stabilized operational amplifier. Low-frequency gain $\doteqdot -10^8$, gain at $1\,kHz \doteqdot -2 \times 10^3$, input offset $\doteqdot 10\ \mu V/°C$, and input current $< 10^{-9}\,A$. The broken line indicates integrator connections.

Required gain. The specified maximum error in linearity is 1 per cent. Thus, from eqn. (6.38),

$$\frac{t}{2[CR(1+A)]} \leqslant \frac{1}{100},$$

or

$$A + 1 = \frac{100}{2 \times 10^{-4}} = 0.5 \times 10^6.$$

While this magnitude of gain is difficult to obtain with a single operational amplifier, it is easily provided by the compound arrangement of Fig. 6.73.

Error introduced by bias current. If the amplifier requires bias current, this could be required to be supplied from the capacitor. For an output voltage v_o,

$$i = C\frac{dv_o}{dt}.$$

For the specified error, the maximum permissible output voltage due to i is 0.1 V in 1 s, i.e. $\mathrm{d}v_o/\mathrm{d}t = 0.1$ V/s. Thus, the maximum value for i is $0.1 \times 10^{-8} = 10^{-9}$ A. This is much less than the bias current for a general-purpose operational amplifier, but is within the specification of a FET input amplifier. However, the system of Fig. 6.73b isolates the bias current from the summing point.

A second consideration is the current generated by the offset voltage across the 10 kΩ resistor R,

$$i = \frac{V_{DI}}{R} \quad \text{or} \quad V_{DI} = 10^{-9}\,\text{A} \times 10\,\text{k}\Omega = 10^{-5}\,\text{V}.$$

This input offset could not be achieved by the use of a monolithic amplifier, but is possible using a chopper system.

Auxiliary amplifier gain. Using a standard amplifier with input offset of 4 mV, the auxiliary amplifier gain should be about 10^3 to reduce the offset to the required value. From Fig. 6.32, a bandwidth of 1 kHz is obtained with a gain of 10^3 for a series–parallel amplifier. This limits the chopper frequency to about 200 Hz. The low-frequency limit of 10 Hz is adequate, and the coupling network and bias elements are selected accordingly, using the techniques of Fig. 6.38.

Output filter for auxiliary amplifier. The auxiliary amplifier output will nominally be 4 mV to cancel the offset voltage of the main amplifier. This will be in the form of rectangular pulses, as in Fig. 6.71b, and the estimated magnitude of the sawtooth waveform of the filtered output is,

$$V = \frac{V_r t}{CR} \quad \text{or} \quad \frac{V}{V_r} = \frac{t}{CR}.$$

If the ripple is to be 10^{-4} of the input, CR should be $10^4 \times t$, where t is the half period, 2.5 ms. Thus CR should be about 25 s. Let the filter components be $C_f = 100\ \mu\text{F}$ and $R_f = 220\ \text{k}\Omega$.

Input filter. The amplifier noise is reduced if the input chopper is separated from the summing point with a filter. The "T" form is necessary to prevent both the summing point and the chopper from being shunted by the filter capacitor.

Limiting diodes. The summing point and chopper output voltages are limited to ±0.5 V by silicon diodes. This reduces the settling time at switch-on, and after overloads.

Coupling for the main amplifier. The coupling is capacitive to remove the bias current from the summing point. The corner frequency thus introduced is not particularly critical, but the gain should be adequate at a sufficiently low frequency, so that the main amplifier can be effective before the auxiliary amplifier gain has fallen significantly. If the time constant is 0.1 s, this would occur at a frequency two decades above the chopper filter cut-off. Keeping the resistors to the inverting and non-inverting inputs equal, a coupling capacitor of $C = 1 \, \mu\text{F}$ and $R = 220 \, \text{k}\Omega$ are appropriate.

The complete system is shown in Fig. 6.74. Note that the chopper amplifier has signal inversion because of the inversion of the chopper drives indicated in Fig. 6.71a.

6.10.   Stabilization against oscillation[43]

For negative feedback amplifiers, the signal fed back from the output is subtracted from the input signal. If it is added, the feedback is positive. A general expression for the closed-loop gain of a negative feedback system is, from eqn. (6.23),

$$G = \frac{A}{1 + A\beta},$$

where the loop gain $A\beta$ is a phasor quantity, having both magnitude and phase angle. When this angle, as shown in Fig. 6.75, is 180° the feedback is no longer negative but positive. If the loop gain $A\beta = 1 \angle -180° = -1$, the closed loop gain becomes

$$G = \frac{A}{1 + A\beta} = \frac{A}{1 - 1} = \infty.$$

The gain becomes infinite and the system will oscillate, producing a sinusoidal output even though the input is zero. If the gain is greater than unity at the frequency at which the angle of $A\beta$ is $-180°$, the system will usually oscillate (at a frequency close to that value) in a non-linear manner, i.e. with non-sinusoidal form. In Fig. 6.75 negative feedback is restricted to frequencies below the second breakpoint at $10^5 \, \text{Hz}$ and loop gains of about 100.

If high loop gains are required, such as for a unity gain follower where typically, $A\beta = A = 10^5$, it is necessary to modify the amplifier open-loop characteristic so that the second breakpoint lies below the

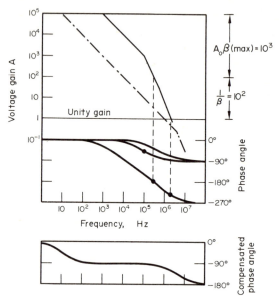

Fig. 6.75. Amplifier open-loop characteristics. The maximum loop gain possible without oscillation is $A_0\beta = 10^3$, at which point the phase angle is $-180°$. The compensated curve allows loop gains up to 10^5 where β is unity.

unity gain line. Many operational amplifiers have this compensation incorporated in their design, but others require the addition of external components for this purpose. While this is inconvenient, it does mean that sometimes larger bandwidths can be obtained, as the compensation can be selected for a particular case. For the system of Fig. 6.75, a closed-loop gain of 1000 can be obtained with a bandwidth of 10^5 Hz for the uncompensated system, but this is reduced to 10^3 Hz for the internally stabilized amplifier.

6.11.   Active resistor–capacitor filters

6.11.1.   First-order filters

These can be constructed readily, using operational amplifiers. Figure 6.76a requires only two elements apart from the amplifier, and has unity gain.

$$\frac{v_0}{v_1}(s) = \frac{1}{1 + (s/\omega_0)},$$
(6.44)

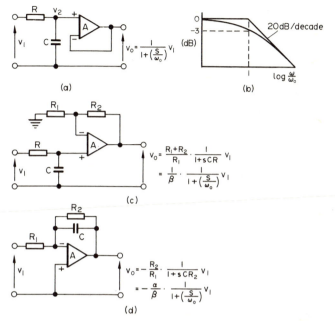

Fig. 6.76. First-order low-pass filters. (a) Simple lag with voltage follower buffer. (b) First-order low-pass response. (c) Voltage amplifier low-pass system. (d) Inverting amplifier low-pass system.

where $\omega_0 = 1/CR$, and in terms of real frequency, writing $s = j\omega$,

$$\frac{v_0}{v_1}(j\omega) = \frac{1}{1 + j(\omega/\omega_0)}. \qquad (6.45)$$

The arrangements (c) and (d) in Fig. 6.76 have β less than unity, and therefore provide voltage gain. These are *first-order* systems, since they are all represented by expressions in which the s in the

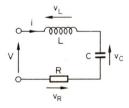

Fig. 6.77. Series LCR circuit. The three voltage responses, corresponding to low-pass, band-pass and high-pass filter characteristics are given in Fig. 6.78.

denominator is of the first power. High-pass filters can be formed by the interchange of R and C in the systems of (a) and (c), but system (d) poses certain problems.

6.11.2. Basic second-order filters

The current flowing in the series LCR circuit of Fig. 6.77 is

$$i = \frac{v}{sL + 1/sC + R},\qquad\qquad (6.46)$$

$$= \frac{sC}{s^2LC + sCR + 1}\, v.$$

Writing,

$$\omega_0{}^2 = \frac{1}{LC} \quad \text{and} \quad Q = \frac{\omega_0 L}{R} = \frac{1}{\omega_0 CR},$$

$$i = \frac{sC}{\left(\dfrac{s}{\omega_0}\right)^2 + \left(\dfrac{s}{\omega_0}\right)\dfrac{1}{Q} + 1}\, v. \qquad\qquad (6.47)$$

The voltage across the capacitor is,

$$v_C = \frac{i}{sC} = \frac{1}{\left(\dfrac{s}{\omega_0}\right)^2 + \left(\dfrac{s}{\omega_0}\right)\dfrac{1}{Q} + 1}\, v. \qquad\qquad (6.48)$$

Similarly, the voltages across the resistor and inductor are

$$v_R = Ri = \frac{\left(\dfrac{s}{\omega_0}\right)\dfrac{1}{Q}}{\left(\dfrac{s}{\omega_0}\right)^2 + \left(\dfrac{s}{\omega_0}\right)\dfrac{1}{Q} + 1}\, v, \qquad\qquad (6.49)$$

and

$$v_L = sLi = \frac{\left(\dfrac{s}{\omega_0}\right)^2}{\left(\dfrac{s}{\omega_0}\right)^2 + \left(\dfrac{s}{\omega_0}\right)\dfrac{1}{Q} + 1}\, v. \qquad\qquad (6.50)$$

In terms of real frequency,

$$\frac{v_C}{v} = \frac{1}{-\left(\frac{\omega}{\omega_0}\right)^2 + j\left(\frac{\omega}{\omega_0}\right)\frac{1}{Q} + 1}, \tag{6.51}$$

$$= \frac{1}{\left[1 - \left(\frac{\omega}{\omega_0}\right)^2\right] + j\left(\frac{\omega}{\omega_0}\right)\frac{1}{Q}}. \tag{6.52}$$

Similarly,

$$\frac{v_R}{v} = \frac{j\left(\frac{\omega}{\omega_0}\right)\frac{1}{Q}}{\left[1 - \left(\frac{\omega}{\omega_0}\right)^2\right] + j\left(\frac{\omega}{\omega_0}\right)\frac{1}{Q}}, \tag{6.53}$$

$$\frac{v_L}{v} = \frac{-\left(\frac{\omega}{\omega_0}\right)^2}{\left[1 - \left(\frac{\omega}{\omega_0}\right)^2\right] + j\left(\frac{\omega}{\omega_0}\right)\frac{1}{Q}}. \tag{6.54}$$

The denominators of these three equations are identical and the differences between them are due only to the numerator terms. Due to the action of j and j^2, these essentially rotate the responses

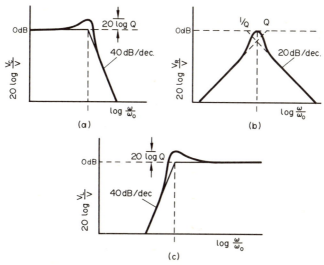

Fig. 6.78. Basic second-order responses. (a) Low-pass. (b) Band-pass. (c) High-pass.

through 90°. The basic response is obtained with the capacitor voltage, and is the low pass curve of Fig. 6.78a. If multiplied by $j\omega/\omega_0$ and a scaling factor, the band-pass characteristic of Fig. 6.78b is obtained. A scaling factor $1/\omega_0 Q$, ensures that the response is unity at resonance. A further multiplication by $j\omega/\omega_0$ gives the high pass filter characteristic of Fig. 6.78c.

6.11.3. Resistance–capacitance form of second-order system

Figure 6.79a shows a system for which the following equations represent the currents leaving nodes 2 and 3:

$$- Y_1 v_1 + (Y_1 + Y_2 + Y_3)v_2 - Y_3 v_3 = 0,$$
$$- Y_3 v_2 + (Y_3 + Y_4)v_3 = 0.$$

Eliminating v_2, and writing $v_3 = v_0$,

$$\frac{v_0}{v_1} = \frac{Y_1 Y_3}{Y_1 Y_3 + Y_1 Y_4 + Y_2 Y_3 + Y_2 Y_4 + Y_3 Y_4}. \qquad (6.55)$$

If this is to represent a low pass filter, the numerator term must be independent of frequency, i.e. Y_1 and Y_3 must represent resistances.

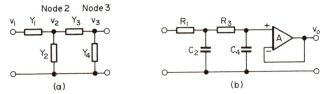

Fig. 6.79. General form of a passive filter. In (b) the voltage follower provides isolation from external loads.

In the denominator, the only product which does not include these is $Y_2 Y_4$. It follows that, for the denominator to contain an s^2 term, Y_2 and Y_4 must be capacitors.

Substituting $Y_1 = 1/R_1$, $Y_3 = 1/R_3$, $Y_2 = sC_2$ and $Y_4 = sC_4$, and rearranging yields

$$\frac{v_0}{v_1} = \frac{1}{s^2 C_2 C_4 R_1 R_3 + s(C_2 R_1 + C_4 R_1 + C_4 R_3) + 1}$$

$$= \frac{1}{\left(\dfrac{s}{\omega_0}\right)^2 + \dfrac{C_2 R_1 + C_4 R_1 + C_4 R_3}{\sqrt{C_2 C_4 R_1 R_3}}\left(\dfrac{s}{\omega_0}\right) + 1}, \qquad (6.56)$$

where

$$\omega_0^2 = \frac{1}{C_2 C_4 R_1 R_3}$$

and the equivalent Q is

$$Q_{eq} = \frac{1}{\omega_0(C_2 R_1 + C_4 R_1 + C_4 R_3)}.$$

The value of Q is limited and not easy to derive. If $R_1 = R_3$ and $C_2 = C_4$, $Q = \frac{1}{3}$. For a *maximally flat* response (a desirable form for Fig. 6.78a in which there is no overshoot) the equivalent Q is 0.707. A minor change to Fig. 6.79b, as shown in Fig. 6.80, forms a system which is much more amenable to design.

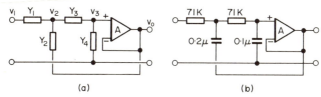

(a)   (b)

Fig. 6.80. (a) General form of a feedback active filter using a voltage follower and (b) a low-pass filter.

6.11.4. Active second-order filter

Currents flowing out of nodes v_2 and v_0 ($= v_3$) are

$$- Y_1 v_1 + (Y_1 + Y_2 + Y_3)v_2 - (Y_2 + Y_3)v_0 = 0,$$
$$- Y_3 v_2 + (Y_3 + Y_4)v_0 = 0.$$

Eliminating the voltage v_2,

$$\frac{v_0}{v_1} = \frac{Y_1 Y_3}{Y_1 Y_3 + Y_1 Y_4 + Y_2 Y_4 + Y_3 Y_4}. \tag{6.57}$$

There is one less term than for the passive case of eqn. (6.55), which increases the flexibility of arranging the elements.

DESIGN EXAMPLE 6.4

Required, a low-pass filter with 100 r/s bandwidth and a maximally flat characteristic.

This implies that $Q = 0.707$ and, in eqn. (6.48), the coefficient of the (s/ω_0) term is 1.414.

The standard form is

$$\frac{v_0}{v_1} = \frac{1}{\left(\dfrac{s}{\omega_0}\right)^2 + \left(\dfrac{s}{\omega_0}\right)\dfrac{1}{Q} + 1},$$

and is compared with eqn. (6.57). $Y_1 Y_3$ must be resistive, and $Y_2 Y_4$ of Fig. 6.80 must be capacitive.

$$\frac{v_0}{v_1} = \frac{\dfrac{1}{R_1 R_3}}{\dfrac{1}{R_1 R_3} + \dfrac{sC_4}{R_1} + s^2 C_2 C_4 + \dfrac{sC_4}{R_3}},$$

$$= \frac{1}{s^2 R_1 R_3 C_2 C_4 + s(C_4 R_1 + C_4 R_3) + 1},$$

$$= \frac{1}{\left(\dfrac{s}{\omega_0}\right)^2 + \left(\dfrac{s}{\omega_0}\right)(C_4 R_1 + C_4 R_3)\omega_0 + 1}. \qquad (6.58)$$

Comparing coefficients,

$$1/Q = C_4(R_1 + R_3)\omega_0 \quad \text{and} \quad \omega_0 = 1/\sqrt{R_1 R_3 C_2 C_4}.$$

Let $C_4 = 0.1\,\mu\text{F}$,

$$(R_1 + R_3) = \frac{1}{QC_4\omega_0} = \frac{1.414}{10^{-7}\times 10^2} = 141.4\,\text{k}\Omega.$$

If $R_1 = R_3 = 70.7\,\text{k}\Omega$,

$$C_2 = \frac{1}{\omega_0^2 R_1 R_3 C_4} = \frac{1}{10^4 \times (70.7)^2 \times 10^6 \times 10^{-7}} = 0.2\,\mu\text{F}.$$

The completed filter is shown in Fig. 6.80b. A 741 operational amplifier would perform satisfactorily as the voltage follower.

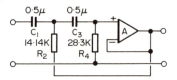

Fig. 6.81. High-pass filter with maximally flat response and low-frequency bandwidth of 100 r/s (15.9 Hz).

DESIGN EXAMPLE 6.5

High-pass filter. The s^2 term required for the numerator of the high-pass expression of eqn. (6.54) is obtained if Y_1 and Y_3 in Fig. 6.80a are capacitors. The arrangement is shown in Fig. 6.81. Making suitable substitution in eqn. (6.55),

$$\frac{v_0}{v_1} = \frac{s^2 C_1 C_3}{s^2 C_1 C_3 + \dfrac{sC_1}{R_4} + \dfrac{sC_3}{R_4} + \dfrac{1}{R_2 R_4}},$$

$$= \frac{\left(\dfrac{s}{\omega_0}\right)^2}{\left(\dfrac{s}{\omega_0}\right)^2 + \left(\dfrac{s}{\omega_0}\right)\omega_0(C_1 R_2 + C_3 R_2) + 1}. \tag{6.59}$$

Comparing coefficients, as previously, in this case

$$1/Q = R_2(C_1 + C_3)\omega_0 \quad \text{where} \quad \omega_0 = 1/\sqrt{C_1 C_3 R_2 R_4}.$$

Let $C_1 = C_3 = 0.5\ \mu\text{F}$,

$$R_2 = \frac{1.414}{10^{-6} \times 10^2} = 14.14\ \text{k}\Omega.$$

The operational amplifier will function most satisfactorily with resistors in the range $10\ \text{k}\Omega$ to $100\ \text{k}\Omega$.

$$R_4 = \frac{1}{\omega_0^2 C_1 C_3 R_2} = \frac{1}{10^4 \times (0.5)^2 \times 10^{-12} \times 14.14 \times 10^3},$$
$$= 28.3\ \text{k}\Omega.$$

6.11.5. Higher-order filters

Combinations of first-order and second-order filters enable systems of any order to be formed. Figure 6.82 shows the form of a third-order filter which is made up of a first-order section together with one of second order. The appropriate coefficients of the

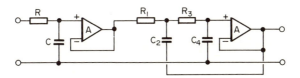

Fig. 6.82. Third-order low-pass filter.

Table 6.3. Maximally flat (Butterworth) polynomials

First order	$\left(\dfrac{s}{\omega_0}\right)+1$
Second order	$\left(\dfrac{s}{\omega_0}\right)^2+1.414\left(\dfrac{s}{\omega_0}\right)+1$
Third order	$\left[\left(\dfrac{s}{\omega_0}\right)+1\right]\left[\left(\dfrac{s}{\omega_0}\right)^2+\left(\dfrac{s}{\omega_0}\right)+1\right]$
Fourth order	$\left[\left(\dfrac{s}{\omega_0}\right)^2+0.765\left(\dfrac{s}{\omega_0}\right)+1\right]\left[\left(\dfrac{s}{\omega_0}\right)^2+1.848\left(\dfrac{s}{\omega_0}\right)+1\right]$

denominator expressions, representing the equivalent value of $1/Q$, are given in Table 6.3.

Band-pass and band-rejection filters. Cascaded high-pass and low-pass filters with overlapping pass bands provide a band-pass characteristic, as shown in Fig. 6.83a. Figure 6.83b shows how a band-rejection characteristic can be formed.

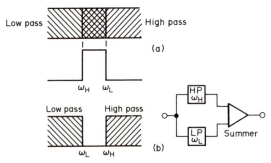

Fig. 6.83. (a) Band-pass characteristic obtained from a cascade connection of high-pass and low-pass filters. Bandwidth $= \omega_L - \omega_H (\omega_H < \omega_L)$. (b) Parallel combination of high-pass and low-pass filters to give a band-rejection characteristic. Rejection band $= \omega_H - \omega_L. (\omega_H > \omega_L)$.

6.11.6. Multiple feedback band-pass filter

A single filter of the types described in § 6.11.4 cannot be arranged to have the band-pass characteristic of Fig. 6.78b. However, with the inclusion of one more passive element, the system of Fig. 6.84

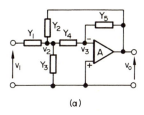 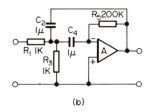

(a)   (b)

Fig. 6.84. Band-pass filter. (a) v_2 is the node 2 voltage. Node 3 is a virtual earth with $v_3 \doteq 0$. (b) Calculated band-pass component values.

can be formed which can, with suitable selection of elements, operate as any of the basic second order filters.

In Fig. 6.84a, summing the currents leaving node 2 and equating to zero,

$$- Y_1 v_1 + (Y_1 + Y_2 + Y_3 + Y_4)v_2 - Y_2 v_0 = 0.$$

Similarly for node 3, where the amplifier input is a virtual earth and $v_3 = 0$,

$$- Y_4 v_2 - Y_5 v_0 = 0.$$

Using this equation to eliminate v_2,

$$v_0 \left[Y_2 + \frac{Y_5}{Y_4}(Y_1 + Y_2 + Y_3 + Y_4) \right] = - Y_1 v_1,$$

and rearranging,

$$v_0 = \frac{Y_1 Y_4}{Y_2 Y_4 + Y_5(Y_1 + Y_2 + Y_3 + Y_4)} v_1. \tag{6.60}$$

From eqn. (6.49), the band-pass characteristic is

$$\frac{v_0}{v_1} = \frac{\left(\dfrac{s}{\omega_0}\right)\dfrac{1}{Q}}{\left(\dfrac{s}{\omega_0}\right)^2 + \left(\dfrac{s}{\omega_0}\right)\dfrac{1}{Q} + 1}.$$

Either Y_1 or Y_4 must be capacitive, to provide the s term in the numerator. If Y_2 and Y_4 both represent capacitors, the product $Y_2 Y_4$ will provide the s^2 term in the denominator. Making suitable substitution in eqn. (6.60),

$$\frac{v_0}{v_1} = -\frac{\dfrac{sC_4}{R_1}}{s^2C_2C_4 + s\left(\dfrac{C_2+C_4}{R_5}\right) + \dfrac{1}{R_1R_5} + \dfrac{1}{R_3R_5}},$$

$$= -\frac{(sC_4R_5R)/R_1}{s^2C_2C_4R_5R + s(C_2+C_4)R + 1}, \tag{6.61}$$

where R represents the parallel combination of R_1 and R_3.

Equating coefficients with the standard form,

$$C_2C_4R_5R = \frac{1}{\omega_0^2}, \tag{6.62}$$

$$(C_2+C_4)R = \frac{1}{\omega_0 Q}, \tag{6.63}$$

$$\frac{C_4R_5R}{R_1} = \frac{A_0}{\omega_0 Q}. \tag{6.64}$$

There are five unknown elements and three independent equations. The coefficients of the numerator and denominator s terms are not equal, and their ratio determines the gain at the centre frequency ω_0.

DESIGN EXAMPLE 6.6

Required, a second-order band-pass filter with 100 r/s centre frequency and a bandwidth of 10 r/s. Gain at the centre frequency is to be 20.

As there are three equations and five unknowns, the value of two components can be selected arbitrarily. Let $C_2 = C_4 = 1\,\mu F$.

$$R = \frac{1}{\omega_0 Q(C_2+C_4)} = \frac{1}{10^2 \times 10 \times 2 \times 10^{-6}} = 500\,\Omega.$$

$$R_5 = \frac{1}{\omega_0^2 C_2C_4R} = \frac{1}{10^4 \times 10^{-12} \times 5 \times 10^2} = 200\,k\Omega.$$

$$R_1 = \frac{\omega_0 Q C_4 R_5 R}{A_0} = \frac{10^2 \times 10 \times 10^{-6} \times 2 \times 10^5 \times 5 \times 10^2}{20} = 1\,k\Omega.$$

$$R_3 = \frac{R_1 R}{R_1 - R} = 1\,k\Omega.$$

The completed design is shown in Fig. 6.84b.

CHAPTER 7

Power Supplies

INTRODUCTION

The most convenient source of power to operate electronic equipment is the supply mains. This has the advantage of cheapness and constancy, when compared with batteries, but a disadvantage is the inevitable introduction of mains frequency noise. The conversion from a.c. to undirectional current can be most efficiently carried out by semiconductor diodes. These have low forward resistance, require no auxiliary power and can be used in applications where it would be difficult to supply the heater power supply to thermionic valves.

7.1. The basic rectifier

In the circuit of Fig. 7.1 the diode conducts on alternate half-cycles and the average (or d.c) value of output voltage is V_R/π. The

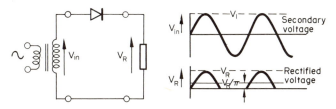

Fig. 7.1. The half-wave rectifier.

voltage applied across the diode during negative half-cycles is known as the inverse voltage and if this exceeds the inverse voltage rating of the component, breakdown may occur. The maximum inverse voltage rating varies from a few volts for small components to several thousand volts for high-voltage diodes.

7.2   The full-wave rectifier

To increase the average value of the output voltage from V_R/π to $2V_R/\pi$ two diodes can be used in a full wave system. One diode conducts on the positive half-cycle of alternating voltage, and the other during the negative half-cycle. Such an arrangement, shown in Fig. 7.2, requires a transformer having a centre tapped secondary winding.

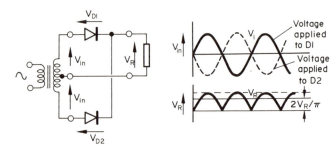

Fig. 7.2. The full-wave rectifier.

Full wave rectification may also be obtained without a centre tapped secondary by making use of the bridge circuit of Fig. 7.3. While thermionic diodes cannot be conveniently used in this configuration, semiconductor diodes, because of their small physical size and no heater requirements, are eminently suitable.

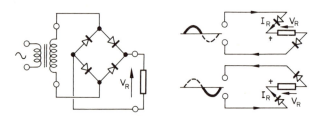

Fig. 7.3. The bridge rectifier. Note the manner in which pairs of diodes operate during alternate half cycles.

7.3.   Effect of load capacitance

Referring to Fig. 7.4 the load capacitor charges when v_{in} is greater than v_R and during the remainder of the cycle supplies the load

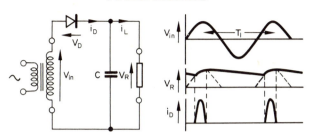

Fig. 7.4. Effect of a reservoir capacitor on the output of a rectifier circuit.

current i_L. If the time constant CR is much greater than the period T_1, the output voltage will not change appreciably over the period. It should be noted that the peak current passed by the diode can be many times the load current.

Output ripple

The output voltage changes during the period and this change constitutes the ripple output. Provided that the CR time constant is much greater than the period $T_1 = 1/f$, and consequently diode current only flows for a short time, the ripple approximates to a sawtooth waveform as shown in Fig. 7.5.

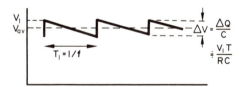

Fig. 7.5. Output ripple. If the CR time constant is much greater than $T = 1/f$, output ripple approximates to a sawtooth waveform.

The change in charge on the capacitor,

$$\Delta Q = \Delta VC = I_L T_1,$$

where I_L is the average load current.
Thus,

$$\Delta V = \frac{I_L T_1}{C} = \frac{V_{av} T_1}{CR} \quad \text{(since } I_L = V_{av}/R\text{)}. \tag{7.1}$$

The average value of output voltage,

$$V_{av} = V_1 - \frac{V_{av}T_1}{2RC} \doteq V_1\left(1 - \frac{T_1}{2RC}\right) \quad (\text{since } V_{av} \doteq V_1).$$

Therefore

$$V_{av} = V_1\left(1 - \frac{1}{2fRC}\right). \tag{7.2}$$

For full wave rectification the ripple frequency is twice the mains frequency, i.e. $T_2 = 1/2f$. In this case the peak to peak ripple voltage,

$$\Delta V = \frac{V_1}{2fRC}. \tag{7.3}$$

Example. A full wave rectifier supplied from a mains source of $f = 50$ Hz and having a peak value $V_1 = 100$ V. If $C = 100$ μF and the load current $I_L = 10$ mA,

$$\Delta V = \frac{V_1}{2fRC} = \frac{100}{2 \times 50 \times 10^4 \times 10^{-4}} = 1 \text{ V}.$$

Percentage ripple $= \Delta V/V_1 \times 100 = 1$ per cent.

Output filter for ripple reduction. The ripple voltage may be reduced by using a low pass filter which, in its simplest form, is the series resistor and shunt capacitor of Fig. 7.6. This is a voltage-dividing network in which the output is developed across the capacitor, which is selected to have a much lower impedance than R.

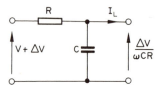

Fig. 7.6. Output filter for ripple reduction. Ripple reduction factor $\gamma = 1/\omega CR$.

A disadvantage of the system is that the load current flows through R, increasing the power-supply resistance. The output voltage will therefore fall as the load current is increased. For R–C smoothing, the ripple reduction factor,

$$\gamma = 1/\omega CR. \tag{7.4}$$

7.4. *L–C* smoothing filter

If an inductance is used in place of the resistance, as in Fig. 7.7, two advantages result. Firstly, the d.c. voltage drop is greatly reduced because of the low resistance of the choke. Secondly, the impedance of the choke is proportional to frequency. Thus, the output ripple is reduced from ΔV to $\Delta V/\omega_r^2 LC$, where ω_r is 2π times the ripple frequency.

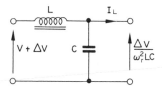

Fig. 7.7. *L–C* smoothing filter. Ripple reduction factor $\gamma = 1/\omega^2 LC$.

For *L–C* smoothing, the ripple reduction factor

$$\gamma = 1/\omega_r^2 LC. \tag{7.5}$$

Referring to the previous example, if the percentage ripple is to be reduced from 1 to 0.1 per cent,

$$\omega_r^2 LC = 10, \quad \text{or} \quad L = 10/\omega_r^2 C.$$

Thus, for a ripple frequency of 100 Hz and $C = 10\ \mu$F, $L = 2.5$ H.

7.5. Choke input filter

When the filter of Fig. 7.7 is used directly with the full wave rectifier of Fig. 7.2 the power supply is known as a choke (or inductance) input type. The filter selects the average component of the rectifier output but removes the ripple.

From Fourier analysis, the series expression for the rectifier output voltage is

$$v = \frac{4V_1}{\pi}\left[\frac{1}{2} + \frac{\cos 2\omega t}{3} - \frac{\cos 4\omega t}{15} + \ldots\right], \tag{7.6}$$

where $\omega = 2\pi$ times the supply frequency.

The average, or d.c. component, is $2V_1/\pi = 0.64 V_1$.

The lowest frequency ripple component has an amplitude of

$4V_1/3\pi$ and is twice the supply frequency. This is the major component of the ripple.

The load current

$$I_R = \frac{V_R}{R} = \frac{2V_1}{\pi R}. \tag{7.7}$$

If it is assumed that the capacitor has a very low impedance at the ripple frequency, the principal ripple component

$$I_c = \frac{4V_1}{3\pi} \frac{1}{2\omega L}. \tag{7.8}$$

This analysis is only valid if the load current I_R is always greater than i_c so that one or other of the rectifiers is conducting at all times, producing the current and voltage waveforms of Fig. 7.8.

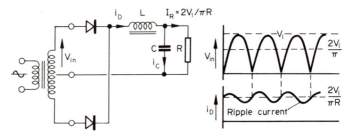

Fig. 7.8. Full-wave rectifier with choke input filter. Provides good regulation and low rectifier peak currents, but relatively low output voltages.

$$\text{Output ripple voltage} = \frac{I_c}{2\omega C} = \frac{V_1}{3\pi\omega^2 LC} \quad \text{[from eqn. (7.8)]},$$

$$\doteqdot \frac{0.1V_1}{\omega^2 LC}. \tag{7.9}$$

The ripple is thus independent of the load current which is not the case when a reservoir capacitor is used.

Example. For $\omega = 2\pi 50$ r/s, $L = 2.5$ H, $C = 100\ \mu$F and $V_1 = 100$ V, the output ripple voltage is 0.8 V peak-to-peak. The minimum current for correct operation is $I_R \geqslant I_C$. Thus, to determine the maximum value of R, equate eqns. (7.7) and (7.8),

$$\frac{2V_1}{\pi R} = \frac{4V_1}{3\pi} \frac{1}{2\omega L},$$

from which, $R = 3\omega L = 2.4\,\mathrm{k\Omega}$. If R is more than this value, the inductor is unable to store sufficient energy to ensure that one rectifier is conducting at all times.

In general, choke input filters have good voltage regulation and low rectifier peak currents but give relatively low output voltages. The use of a reservoir capacitor, as in Fig. 7.9, provides a capacitor input filter which has high output voltages but poor regulation and high rectifier peak currents. Capacitor input filters are used where the load is relatively constant as, for instance, in radio receivers. Comparison of the two types of filter circuits is made in the graph of Fig. 7.10.

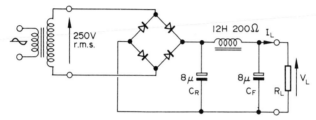

Fig. 7.9. Full-wave rectifier with capacitor input filter. Provides high output voltages, but has high rectifier peak currents and relatively poor regulation.

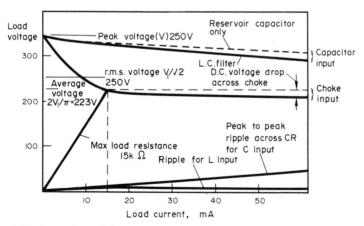

Fig. 7.10. Comparison of the performance of the two types of output filter circuits. The output voltage is the same for both systems under zero load conditions, but for the choke input filter it falls off rapidly until the effective load resistance is 15 kΩ. Thereafter it remains constant.

7.6.   Voltage multipliers

Two rectifiers of the type shown in Fig. 7.4 may be used with the same transformer winding. If the diodes are connected in opposite manner, as in Fig. 7.11, the two d.c. outputs are effectively added giving an output voltage approaching twice the peak input voltage.

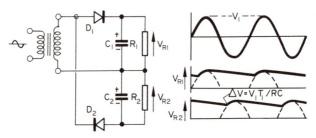

Fig. 7.11. The voltage doubler. If the load current is small, the output voltage is twice the peak value of input voltage.

An alternative form of voltage multiplier is given in Fig. 7.12. This has a common connection between input and output, which can be a desirable feature in some applications. On negative half-cycles of V_1, C_1 charges up to the peak value of V_1 through D_1. On positive half-cycles D_1 is non-conducting and the anode of D_2 is raised to twice the peak value of V_1. After a number of cycles C_2 charges to $2V_1$.

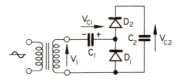

Fig. 7.12. Alternative form of voltage doubler.

Any number of stages may be employed in this circuit arrangement, enabling very large voltages to be developed from low-voltage sources. In Fig. 7.13, C_3 will charge to V_{C2} through D_3 and then will be raised $2V_1$ by the charge on C_1. The voltage across C_3 will charge C_4 through D_4. Similarly, C_5 will charge to the voltage across C_4 through

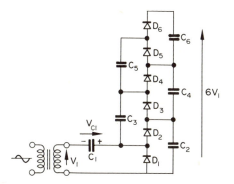

Fig. 7.13. The voltage multipler. The circuit is a development of Fig. 7.12 and may be extended to provide very large voltages.

D_5 and then be raised $2V_1$ by C_3. Each of the output capacitors is charged to $2V_1$ thus providing an output voltage 6 times the peak input voltage.

7.7. Voltage stabilization

The power supplies so far described have output voltages determined by two main factors: (a) the supply voltage and (b) the load current drawn. Changes in either of these will cause the output voltage to change. In order to make the output voltage relatively insensitive to variations in supply voltage, or load current, some form of voltage stabilization is necessary.

Gas discharge tube[44]

A simple way of ensuring that the output voltage is stable is to use the constant voltage developed across a gas discharge, as in Fig. 7.14.

DESIGN EXAMPLE 7.1

Required, a nominal 100-V supply for a 25-mA load current derived from a 200-V source.

A suitable discharge tube is the 108C1 (the 108 indicates the operating voltage), having an operating current range of 5–30 mA and requiring a striking voltage of 140 V.

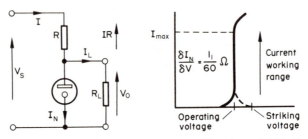

Fig. 7.14. Use of a gas-discharge tube to provide voltage stabilization.

In order to accommodate changes in load current it is desirable to operate the tube near the middle of its current range. Let I_N be 20 mA. From Fig. 7.14, the input current, $I_N + I_L = 20 + 25 = 45$ mA.

The value of the series resistor R, necessary to drop the voltage from V_S to V_0, is given by:

$$R = \frac{V_S - V_0}{I_N + I_L} = \frac{92 \text{ V}}{45 \text{ mA}} \doteq 2 \text{ k}\Omega.$$

As I_L is reduced, the current through the tube increases. Thus the load current can vary from 25 to 40 mA without an appreciable change in the output voltage.

Differential resistance.   This is the change in tube voltage for a given change in tube current and is of the order of 100 Ω. Thus a change of 5 mA will change the output voltage by approximately 0.5 V.

Striking voltage.   As shown in Fig. 7.14, a higher voltage than the operating voltage is required to initiate the discharge, and V_S must be sufficient for this purpose. Some discharge tubes have an auxiliary trigger electrode which is used for striking the discharge.

The range of discharge tube stabilizers is from 50 to 150 V, but higher voltages can be stabilized by using two tubes in series. In this case provision must be made for striking one tube independently of the other. A method is shown in Fig. 7.15 in which R_S provides a path for striking the lower regulator. The upper tube strikes subsequently, due to the source voltage.

Voltage reference tubes.   The discharge tube, by operating at a specified current, gives a defined voltage that can be used as a reference voltage source. Special tubes are available for this pur-

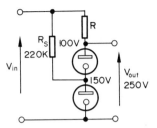

Fig. 7.15. Voltage stabilization using two gas-discharge tubes in series. The resistor R_s provides a path for striking the lower regulator.

pose and a common reference voltage is 85 V. (See Design Example 7.5.)

High-voltage stabilizers. The corona discharge at high voltage can be used to stabilize voltages of the order of 1000 V. Operation is in a manner similar to that described for gas discharge tubes but operating current levels are much lower.

7.8. Semiconductor stabilizer diodes

Junction diodes can be produced with a well-defined breakdown voltage when operated with reverse voltage applied. A typical characteristic for a silicon breakdown diode is given in Fig. 7.16. The usual range of operation is from 3 to 20 V. The manner of application is similar to that of gas discharge tubes but no striking voltage is required. Large currents can be passed by breakdown diodes but, since the device maintains a constant voltage across itself, the maximum safe current is determined by the power dissipation of the

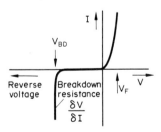

Fig. 7.16. Typical characteristic of a silicon-breakdown diode.

device. This is from 200 mW for a small free mounted device to several watts for a stud mounted diode. ·

The breakdown voltage is a function of temperature with a typical variation of from -2 to $+8$ mV/°C. Diodes with temperature coefficients of the order of 10 μV/°C can be obtained for use as voltage reference sources. When used for this purpose the diode should be operated from a constant current supply.

DESIGN EXAMPLE 7.2

Required, from a 20-V source, a stabilized voltage supply having a nominal voltage of 6.8 V and providing a load current of 15 mA ± 10 mA.

The circuit arrangement is shown in Fig. 7.17a while in Fig. 7.17b is drawn an approximation of the supply output.

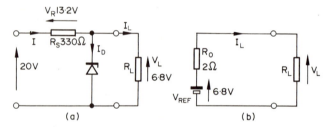

Fig. 7.17. (a) Circuit arrangement of Design Example 7.2, with (b) an approximate representation of the supply output.

A 1S7068A diode has a nominal breakdown voltage of 6.8 V and an incremental resistance, $\delta V/\delta I = 2\,\Omega$ at a current of 15 mA.

The maximum load current will flow when the diode current is a minimum. If the minimum diode current is 15 mA, then the current drawn from the source is

$$I = I_L + I_D = 25\text{ mA} + 15\text{ mA} = 40\text{ mA}.$$

The voltage to be dropped across the series resistor is

$$V_R = V_S - V_{BD} = 20\text{ V} - 6.8\text{ V} = 13.2\text{ V}.$$

$$R_S = \frac{V_R}{I} = \frac{13.2\text{ V}}{40\text{ mA}} = 330\,\Omega.$$

The output voltage falls approximately $\Delta V_L = R_{out}\Delta I_L$ as the load current increases from its minimum to its maximum value.

Thus, $\Delta V_L = 2 \times 20 \times 10^{-3} = 0.04$ V.

Under these conditions the maximum possible dissipation in the diode is $IV_L \doteqdot 300$ mW, which is well within the stated dissipation of the device.

7.9. Emitter follower as a voltage stabilizer

As the output voltage of an emitter follower closely follows the input base voltage, it can be used to isolate the voltage reference from the load, thus enabling large currents to be supplied without appreciably modifying the reference voltage. Such a system is shown in Fig. 7.18a.

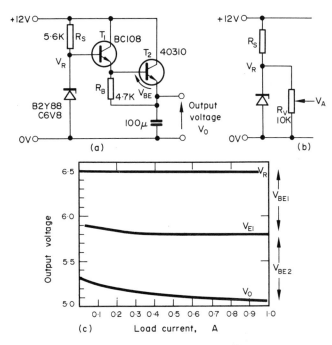

Fig. 7.18. (a) Compound emitter follower voltage regulator. (b) Adjustable voltage source V_A. (c) Voltage load–current relationships.

DESIGN EXAMPLE 7.3

Required, a 5-V supply for currents up to 1 A from a nominal 12-V source.

A breakdown diode with a nominal voltage of 6.8 V cannot supply this current directly and it is desirable that the current drawn from it should be as small as possible, thus ensuring a constant reference voltage. This should be higher than the required output voltage because of the base–emitter voltage requirements. As shown in Fig. 7.18c, the increase in V_{BE} necessary for the larger load currents causes a fall in output voltage.

Selection of output transistor. The requirements to be met are current, voltage and power dissipation rating. The current gain must be sufficient to reduce loading effects on the reference source to the permitted value. With a compound emitter follower, a current gain of 5×10^3 ensures that the input current is only 0.2 mA when the load current is 1 A. The current gain can be provided by an input transistor with a gain of 100, and a power device with a gain of 50. Under maximum current conditions, the collector dissipation is 1 A at 7 V, i.e. 7 W. The 403 10 with a power rating of 30 W, current rating of 4 A, a voltage rating of 40 V, and with a typical h_{FE} in excess of 50, has adequate current gain.

Bias resistor R_B. When the load current is small, particularly if the current gain of T_2 is high, the collector current for T_1 can be sufficiently reduced to affect the operation of the device. The resistor R_B (Fig. 7.18) draws a relatively constant current, since it has the base–emitter voltage of T_2 across it, thereby ensuring that the emitter current of T_1 is maintained.

Output capacitor. The emitter follower output resistance rises at high frequencies where the current gain is reduced. A capacitor across the output terminals ensures that the output impedance is kept low for high-frequency signals.

Reference voltage. A breakdown diode, such as the BZY88 C6V8, when operated at 1 mA has an incremental resistance of 15 Ω. (This implies that an increase of 1 mA through the device changes the breakdown voltage by 15 mV.) The temperature coefficient for the device is typically 3 mV/°C, and at 1 mA the range of breakdown voltage is from 6.3 V to 6.9 V. The output voltage can be varied using the arrangement of Fig. 7.18b.

Input transistor. A general purpose device with a high current capability such as a BC 108 transistor, is satisfactory for the purpose.

Performance. The variation in output voltage from no load to full load is 4.6 per cent. Figure 7.18c shows that this change is mainly due to the base–emitter voltage fall as the load current is increased.

7.10. Closed-loop system[45]

The fall in output voltages as load current is increased can be compensated by an increase in the reference voltage, but this is only possible for fixed load conditions. However, if the output voltage is compared with the reference voltage, the difference voltage can be used to correct for any output voltage change.

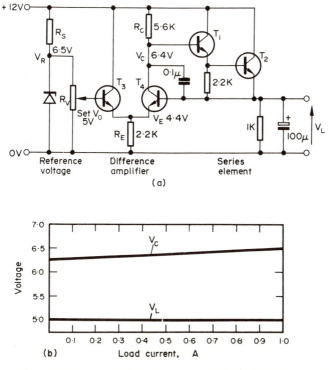

Fig. 7.19. (a) A closed-loop regulator. The output voltage is set by R_v. (b) V_C rises with increasing load current, thereby keeping V_L constant.

In the arrangement of Fig. 7.19 the transistor pair T_3 and T_4 perform as a difference amplifier. The emitter follower, T_3, provides the reference voltage at the emitter of T_4, which amplifies any difference from the output voltage. If the latter is greater than the reference, the voltage V_C will fall, thereby reducing the output voltage. As the system is actuated by the error (i.e. the difference between the actual output and the desired voltage) the performance is determined by the gain, A, of the amplifier.

$$V_o = A(V_R - V_o),$$

$$= \frac{A}{1+A} V_R. \tag{7.10}$$

This is a series–parallel system (§ 6.2a), with β unity and input V_R. The output voltage will follow the input voltage with an error of $1/A$.

DESIGN EXAMPLE 7.4

Required, a closed-loop stabilized supply, using the emitter follower of D.E.7.3. In Fig. 7.19a, the gain of the dfference amplifier is, for small load resistors,

$$A \doteqdot \frac{-h_{fe}R_L}{2h_{ie}}, \tag{7.11}$$

where the $\frac{1}{2}$ term arises because the emitter follower, T_3, effectively inserts a resistance of $1/y_{fe}$ (where $y_{fe} = h_{fe}/h_{ie}$) in the emitter of T_4. The input resistance to T_4 is

$$R_{in} \doteqdot h_{ie} + h_{fe}R_E = 2h_{ie},$$

and the voltage gain is

$$A = \frac{-\text{current gain}}{\text{input resistance}} R_L.$$

For a BC108A transistor, $h_{fe} \doteqdot 200$ and $h_{ie} \doteqdot 5\,\text{k}\Omega$ when the operating current is 1 mA.

R_C is determined by the direct voltage V_C. From Fig. 7.18c this voltage is 6.4 V for 5-V output voltage (i.e. $V_{B1} + V_{B2} + V_o$). The voltage across R_C is 5.6 V and for 1 mA current, $R_C = 5.6\,\text{k}\Omega$. If both T_3 and T_4 are to operate at 1 mA, R_E must be $V_E/2I_E$, where V_E is the emitter voltage of T_4, i.e. $5\,\text{V} - 0.6\,\text{V} = 4.4\,\text{V}$.

$$R_E = \frac{4.4\text{ V}}{2\text{ mA}} = 2.2\text{ k}\Omega.$$

This resistor determines the emitter currents but does not directly affect the voltage gain.

$$A \doteq \frac{-200 \times 5.6\text{ k}\Omega}{2 \times 5\text{ k}\Omega},$$

$$\doteq -100.$$

Performance. The gain of the difference amplifier should reduce the variation in output voltage by a factor of 100, i.e. the 0.2-V change in Fig. 7.18c should be reduced to 2 mV.

Ripple reduction. An important function, that the closed-loop regulator performs, is the reduction in output ripple when the supply is obtained from the a.c. mains supply. For large-current low-voltage supplies, the ripple voltage will usually be sufficiently large for the approximations of Fig. 7.5 to be no longer applicable. It is undesirable to incorporate an *LC* filter section, and the regulator is used to reduce the ripple to the required level. The reservoir capacitor must be of sufficient capacitance to ensure that the voltage does not drop below the minimum level at which the system can operate. This might typically be 8 V, i.e. the output voltage together with a minimum of 3 V across the emitter follower. The required capacitor can be found using Fig. 7.20. A line is drawn from the crest of a half sinusoid (i.e. the peak voltage) to intersect the following one at the minimum allowed voltage, and meet the horizontal axis at a time

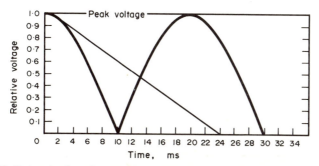

Fig. 7.20. Determination of reservoir capacitance. A line is drawn from the peak voltage crest through the minimum permitted voltage. The load resistance is assumed to be $V_{\text{r.m.s.}}/I = 12\ \Omega$, whence $C = TC/R_L = 24\text{ ms}/12\ \Omega = 2000\ \mu\text{F}$.

interval equivalent to the *RC* time constant. If this is 24 ms, and as a load of 1 A at 12 V is equivalent to 12 Ω, the necessary capacitance is

$$C = \frac{24\ \text{ms}}{12\ \Omega},$$

$$= 2000\ \mu\text{F}.$$

The emitter follower is insensitive to collector voltage changes provided that the minimum voltage is not passed.

Any ripple which does appear at the output, is treated as a change in output voltage and is reduced by the regulator action. In this manner the output ripple can be brought down to millivolt level.

Adjustment of output voltage. As shown in Fig. 7.19a the output voltage can be varied from V_R downwards, the minimum being set by the lowest voltage across R_E which permits satisfactory operation. The relationship is

$$V_0 = \frac{A}{1+A} k V_R \doteqdot k V_R, \quad \text{for } A \gg 1, \tag{7.12}$$

where *k* is the setting on the potentiometer. R_V ranges from 0 to 1. If the output voltage is tapped and compared with the reference voltage V_R, voltages greater than V_R can be obtained.

$$V_o = (V_R - k V_o)A,$$

$$= \frac{A}{1+Ak} V_R,$$

$$\doteqdot \frac{1}{k} V_R \quad \text{if } Ak \gg 1. \tag{7.13}$$

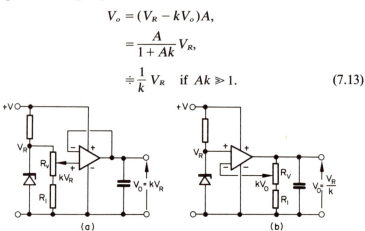

(a)   (b)

Fig. 7.21. Voltage-regulator systems, (a) for voltages less than V_R and (b) for voltages greater than V_R.

In this case, if k is very small the loop gain term Ak is reduced and the performance of the system might be inadequate. There will be a limit placed on the maximum output voltage by the available input voltage. The range of satisfactory operation can be set by a resistor in series with R_V, as in Fig. 7.21.

7.11.   Current limitation

The output current for the closed-loop regulator of Fig. 7.19 can be limited using the method shown in Fig. 7.22. The transistor T_5

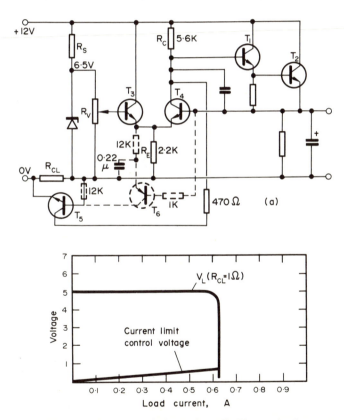

Fig. 7.22. (a) Regulator with current limit transistor T_5. The overload cut-out system is indicated by a broken line. (b) Voltage load–current characteristic. When T_5 conducts, operation changes from constant voltage to constant-current operation.

does not conduct until the voltage across R_{CL} reaches the conduction value. At this current level, T_5 will control the output voltage and reduce it if the current is excessive.

Overload protection. If the output voltage is reduced further, possibly by a short circuit, and the output voltage drops sufficiently below the reference level, T_6 (a *pnp* transistor) conducts and supplies current to T_5, bringing it further into conduction and turning T_4 hard off.

7.12.   Application of operational amplifiers as voltage regulators

The regulator can be analysed as a series–parallel feedback connection. The high gain of an operational amplifier ensures excellent performance when used to replace T_3 and T_4 in Fig. 7.19a. Such a system is shown in Fig. 7.23a, where an emitter follower power stage can be used to increase the output current capability of the amplifier. The power dissipation associated with the output

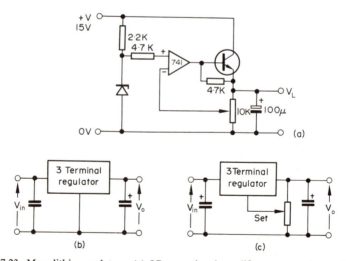

Fig. 7.23. Monolithic regulators. (a) IC operational amplifier connected as a difference amplifier. (b) Three terminal regulator with fixed output voltage. (c) Arrangement to provide a variable output.

transistor is

$$P = (+V - V_L)I_L,$$
$$= 10 \text{ W}, \quad \text{for} \quad I_L = 1 \text{ A}, \quad +V = 15 \text{ V} \quad \text{and} \quad V_L = 5 \text{ V}.$$

A transistor, such as the 40310, on a suitable heat sink would be satisfactory.

7.13. Fully integrated regulators

Among commercially available devices there are precision regulators such as the 723, which will supply 50-mA load current. These can be operated in the two modes shown in Fig. 7.21, either above or below the internal reference voltage. Output current can be increased if an external power transistor is used as in Fig. 7.23.

Another type is the three-terminal regulator. These are operated at specific voltages and have current ratings of 1 A or more. Internal protection against overload is usually provided, the output current being limited when the device temperature reaches the maximum permitted. Some of these types can be used at higher voltages than that specified, but with a loss in performance (see Fig. 7.23).

CHAPTER 8

Oscillators

INTRODUCTION

An electronic oscillator may be described as a device which, whilst obtaining its power from a d.c. source, provides an alternating output without changing its circuit configuration by means of mechanical switching. Such a definition thus excludes rotating machinery and vibrators, etc.

Oscillators fall into two classes: firstly, those which provide a sinusoidal output, and secondly, "relaxation" types whose outputs have a large harmonic content. This latter class is dealt with in Chapter 9 on waveform generators.

8.1. Sinusoidal oscillators—basic considerations

Figure 8.1 represents a current source having resistance R_S, feeding a parallel circuit of R_L, C and L. The current $i(s)$ need not be a specific input but could be noise signals due to thermal agitation or switching transients, etc.

$$v(s) = Z \cdot i(s), \qquad (8.1)$$

$$= \frac{i(s)}{G_S + G_L + sC + (1/sL)}. \qquad (8.2)$$

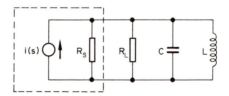

Fig. 8.1. A current source of resistance R_s, feeding a parallel circuit of R_L, C and L.

Multiplying through by s/C,

$$v(s) = \frac{i(s)(s/C)}{s^2 + [s(G_S + G_L)/C] + (1/LC)}. \tag{8.3}$$

The denominator of eqn. (8.3) is the characteristic equation of the circuit, and the performance of the circuit is principally determined by its roots. Thus, let

$$s^2 + \frac{s(G_S + G_L)}{C} + \frac{1}{LC} = 0. \tag{8.4}$$

Solving this equation,

$$s = -\left(\frac{G_S + G_L}{2C}\right) \pm j\sqrt{\left[\frac{1}{LC} - \left(\frac{G_S + G_L}{2C}\right)^2\right]}. \tag{8.5}$$

There are therefore two roots of the form

$$s_1 = -\alpha + j\omega \quad \text{and} \quad s_2 = -\alpha - j\omega, \tag{8.6}$$

and the solution is

$$v(t) = A \exp(-\alpha + j\omega)t + B \exp(-\alpha - j\omega)t. \tag{8.7}$$

The nature of s_1 and s_2 is largely determined by the term $(G_S + G_L)$. Thus, if $(G_S + G_L) = 0$, $s = j\sqrt{(1/LC)}$ and denoting $1/LC$ by ω_0^2,

$$s_1 = +j\omega_0 \quad \text{and} \quad s_2 = -j\omega_0.$$

Hence, for $G_S = G_L$,

$$v(t) = A \exp(j\omega_0 t) + B \exp(-j\omega_0 t), \tag{8.8}$$

and the solution represents an oscillation of ω_0 radians per second of constant amplitude.

More generally, where $(G_S + G_L)$ does not equal 0, given a disturbing signal, oscillations will commence if the roots s_1 and s_2 have imaginary parts, i.e. if in eqn. (8.5), $1/LC$ is greater than $[(G_S + G_L)/2C]^2$. Furthermore, the amplitude of oscillation will increase with time if $(G_S + G_L)$ is less than 0, which implies that G_L is negative. The concept of a negative value of G_L means that energy is supplied to overcome the loss resistance that is always associated with a tuned circuit.

From these considerations, the requirements for a build-up of oscillation, as shown in Fig. 8.2, are as follows:

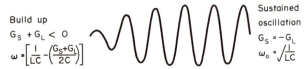

Fig. 8.2. Build-up of an oscillation. The condition for commencement of oscillation is that $G_s + G_L$ is negative, and amplitude stabilizes when $G_s = - G_L$.

(a) A negative resistance component to compensate for tuned circuit losses and provide a divergent oscillation.

(b) A variable resistance component which reduces the real part of the roots to zero when the required amplitude is reached.

(c) A frequency-determining element.

(d) An initiating signal.

8.2. Negative resistance

Defining a negative resistance as an element through which current decreases as the voltage across it increases, it may be represented on a current–voltage characteristic. Thus, in Fig. 8.3, the part of the curve lying between A and B is a negative resistance region having a slope of $-G$.

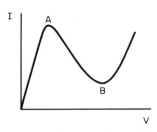

Fig. 8.3. Current–voltage curve showing a negative resistance region AB where, as voltage increases, current decreases.

Any device whose current–voltage characteristics include such a region possesses one of the requirements for oscillation, and by suitable circuit arrangement may be used as an oscillator.

As examples of such devices there are:

(a) Dynatron oscillator using the tetrode negative resistance characteristic.

(b) The transitron oscillation[46] using a pentode with screen and suppressor grids connected.

(c) Solid state devices such as point-contact transistors, thermistors and tunnel diodes.[47]

The dynatron and transitron oscillators are now mostly of historical interest, but the tunnel diode has been used for high-frequency oscillators in the range 100 MHz to 10 GHz.

Alternatively, a negative resistance can be obtained by feedback connection of an amplifier. From eqn. (6.8) the output impedance of an amplifier with feedback is written as:

$$Z_{out} = \frac{Z_{0A}}{1 - A\beta},$$
(8.9)

which is negative for a loop gain $A\beta$ greater than unity. It is this method of obtaining negative resistance which is now most commonly used in the design of oscillators.

Sinusoidal oscillators of the feedback type fall into two classes, inductance–capacitance types, and resistance–capacitance (phaseshift) types. These are considered in detail later in this chapter.

8.3. Amplitude stabilization

It was shown in §8.1 that for oscillations to build up it is necessary that G_L should be negative and greater than G_S. In other words, the damping term of eqn. (8.4) should be negative. In addition the value of G_L must decrease with increasing amplitude of oscillation until, at the required amplitude, $G_S = -G_L$, making the damping term zero.

Alternatively, referring to eqn. (8.9) for feedback amplifiers, for the build-up condition the loop gain $A\beta$ should be greater than unity, and decrease until it reaches unity when the correct amplitude of oscillation is reached. Given a constant feedback factor β, this implies that the amplifier gain must decrease as the signal amplitude increases, and to achieve this some non-linear element is necessary.

Gate leak stabilization

In tuned $L-C$ oscillators, a common method of varying gain with signal amplitude, and thus providing oscillator limitation, is by the

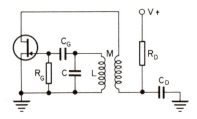

Fig. 8.4. Tuned gate oscillator with gate-leak stabilization. R_D and C_D are decoupling elements.

use of a gate leak. The required non-linearity is provided by the bottom bend of the FET I_D/V_G characteristic. In Fig. 8.4 which represents a tuned gate oscillator, C_G and R_G form the gate leak combination, the time constant of which is chosen to be much greater than the period of oscillation $1/f$. It should not, however, be so great that changes in operating conditions cannot be accepted without affecting circuit performance.

The amplitude stabilizing effect of the gate leak may best be explained with reference to Fig. 8.5 showing a typical build up of oscillation. The effective y_{fs} is given by the slope of the I_D/V_G curve, which is high at $V_G = 0$ and becomes progressively lower as the gate bias is carried more negative. The gate bias is determined by the charge on C_G. Gate current flows on positive peaks of gate signal voltage and charges the capacitor. Due to the CR time constant the

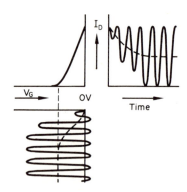

Fig. 8.5. Build up of oscillation with gate-leak stabilization, after the oscillator is switched on at $t = 0$.

charge is additive, and the bias is carried negative thus reducing the gain of the amplifier. The process continues until the y_{fs} is just sufficient to maintain oscillation when the amplitude stabilizes. Should now the gain become reduced, instantaneously the positive signal peaks would cease to carry the gate positive with respect to the source, and no gate current would flow. Some part of the charge on C_G would then leak away, and the effective gate bias would be reduced until the positive peaks again caused gate current to flow. Operation would then stabilize at a smaller amplitude of oscillation.

This form of operation is under *class C conditions* with the operating gate bias beyond cut-off. It causes a discontinuous drain current to flow, but a tuned circuit having a reasonably high Q ensures that the drain voltage is sinusoidal, by providing a low impedance path for harmonic frequencies.

Squegging

At the point of amplitude-stable-oscillation, the time constant is such that the amount of charge leaking away from the capacitor between positive signal peaks is just equal to the amount that is restored when gate current flows. If the time constant is too great, and signal amplitude is excessive, more charge is supplied by gate current than is allowed to leak away between peaks, and the FET is quickly biased to a negative voltage much greater than the cut-off point. Drain current then ceases and oscillations cannot be maintained. The capacitor gradually discharges through the gate leak resistor, until the bias is low enough to allow drain current to flow and oscillations to recommence. The cycle repeats itself and results in intermittent bursts of oscillations known as *squegging*. This condition can normally be prevented by careful choice of gate-leak values. When the oscillator is used in a radio receiver, a large h.t. decoupling resistor also helps to prevent it. Such a resistor causes the oscillator drain voltage to rise with a decrease in gate current, thus removing the cut-off voltage to a higher negative value.

8.4. Survey of feedback $L-C$ oscillators

The most general type of oscillator is the tuned drain-tuned gate arrangement shown in Fig. 8.6. Only the signal paths are drawn, and

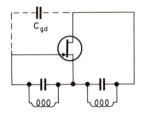

Fig. 8.6. Tuned drain-tuned gate oscillator. Feedback is present through C_{gd}, the gate to drain capacitance.

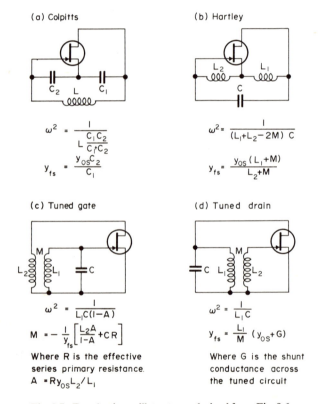

(a) Colpitts

$$\omega^2 = \frac{1}{L\frac{C_1 C_2}{C_1 + C_2}}$$

$$y_{fs} = \frac{y_{os} C_2}{C_1}$$

(b) Hartley

$$\omega^2 = \frac{1}{(L_1 + L_2 - 2M)\, C}$$

$$y_{fs} = \frac{y_{os}\,(L_1 + M)}{L_2 + M}$$

(c) Tuned gate

$$\omega^2 = \frac{1}{L_1 C (1 - A)}$$

$$M = -\frac{1}{y_{fs}}\left[\frac{L_2 A}{1 - A} + C R\right]$$

Where R is the effective series primary resistance.
$A = R y_{os} L_2 / L_1$

(d) Tuned drain

$$\omega^2 = \frac{1}{L_1 C}$$

$$y_{fs} = \frac{L_1}{M}\,(y_{os} + G)$$

Where G is the shunt conductance across the tuned circuit

Fig. 8.7. Four basic oscillator types derived from Fig. 8.6.

feedback is seen to be via the drain to gate capacitance. Figure 8.7 similarly represents four commonly encountered oscillators which are variations on this basic circuit arrangement.

Associated with each circuit are the relevant equations defining the frequency and the conditions for maintenance of oscillation.

The tuned transformer types of oscillator are extensively used as local oscillators in radio receivers. The tuned drain is more stable to h.t. fluctuations than is the tuned gate and in addition has less harmonic content and provides a greater amplitude output. The tuned gate, however, has a more constant amplitude when the oscillator frequency is varied over its tuning range. For use at v.h.f. the Colpitts type is usually preferred, although the Hartley oscillator may also be used at frequencies in excess of 40 MHz. Two common ways of obtaining the operating conditions for these circuits are:

(a) to find the condition under which the loop gain is unity,
(b) to determine the nodal or circuital equations and equate the determinant to zero. (A brief introduction to determinants is given in Appendix A.)

Both methods are demonstrated in the two design examples which follow.

8.5. The tuned drain oscillator

Two basic connections are shown in Fig. 8.8. They differ in the manner in which the voltage is connected to the drain. For the shunt

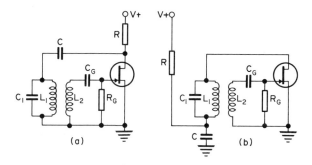

Fig. 8.8. Shunt and series-fed tuned-drain oscillators.

feed system, R isolates the drain from the positive supply, but has the disadvantage of reducing the Q of the tuned circuit. However, it does permit one side of the tuning capacitor C_1 to be connected to ground.

Design considerations

To determine the operating conditions, the arrangement of Fig. 8.7d is redrawn as the small signal equivalent network of Fig. 8.9 in

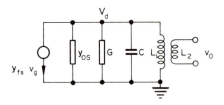

Fig. 8.9. Small-signal equivalent network of Fig. 8.8b. G represents the effective parallel losses of R and the tuned circuit.

which G represents the effective shunt conductance. The nodal equations for this network are (equating current in, to current out):

$$- y_{fs} v_g = v_d \left(y_{os} + sC + G + \frac{1}{sL_1} \right). \tag{8.10}$$

$$v_0 = - s M i_d = - \frac{M}{L_1} v_d. \tag{8.11}$$

Eliminating v_d,

$$- y_{fs} v_g = - \frac{L_1}{M} \left(y_{os} + sC + G + \frac{1}{sL_1} \right) v_0.$$

For oscillation, the output voltage must equal the input voltage, i.e. the loop gain must be unity and $v_o = v_g$.

Thus,

$$- \frac{M}{L_1} y_{fs} + y_{os} + sC + G + \frac{1}{sL_1} = 0,$$

$$- s M y_{fs} + s L_1 y_{os} + s^2 L_1 C + s L_1 G + 1 = 0,$$

and in terms of real frequency (i.e. $s = j\omega$),

$$-\omega^2 L_1 C + 1 + j\omega(L_1 y_{os} + L_1 G - M y_{fs}) = 0. \qquad (8.12)$$

Equating real components,

$$\omega^2 = \frac{1}{L_1 C}. \qquad (8.13)$$

Equating imaginary components,

$$y_{fs} = \frac{L_1}{M}(y_{os} + G). \qquad (8.14)$$

The system will oscillate at a frequency $f = 1/(2\pi\sqrt{LC})$ if the effective y_{fs} is $L_1(y_{os} + G)/M$. In this latter expression there is a sign associated with the mutual inductance, and oscillation will only occur for the arrangement that gives no overall signal inversion. The tuned circuit should have a high Q to minimize the harmonic content (i.e. the waveform distortion), and accordingly L_1 is made large. The gate inductor L_2 should be kept somewhat less than L_1 so that, with its associated stray capacitances, its resonant frequency is much higher than the frequency of oscillation. Otherwise there is the possibility of frequency multiplication. In practice, a winding of one-third to one-half (i.e. an inductance of 1/9 to 1/4) of the main winding is satisfactory. The coupling coefficient is adjusted to give the required mutual inductance.

Design steps
1. Calculate the inductance, which will resonate over the required frequency range. If C is not specified (as it often would be in a variable frequency system) a value should be chosen which is sufficiently large to minimize the effects of stray capacitance, but not so large as to reduce the effective Q of the system, thereby adversely affecting the oscillator waveform and frequency stability. An L/C value of 10^6 is typical.
2. Make the feedback winding approximately one-half the number of primary turns ($L_2 = L_1/4$).
3. Estimate the total effective shunt conductance across the tuned circuit and determine M, using values for the effective y_{fs} of the field effect transistor in eqn. (8.14).
4. Select R_G. This can be 1 MΩ for operation at medium frequency for a junction FET, because of its small reverse saturation

current. C_G is selected to ensure that the time constant $C_G R_G$ is much longer than the oscillation period.

DESIGN EXAMPLE 8.1

Required, a tuned drain oscillator to operate at 1 MHz.

Let the selected FET be a 2N 5458, which has a y_{fs} which ranges from 1.5 to 5 mS.

For $L = 200 \,\mu\text{H}$,

$$C = \frac{1}{f^2 (2\pi)^2 L} = 126.8 \text{ pF}.$$

For fixed frequency operation, the tuned circuit can be resonated at the required frequency by adjusting the position of the ferrite core of the inductor.

The required mutual inductance

$$M = \frac{L_1}{y_{fs}} (y_{os} + G),$$

where G is principally the reciprocal of the dynamic impedance of the tuned circuit. The latter is the product of Q and the branch impedance, i.e. $Q\omega L$.

Assuming a Q of 100,

$$\omega L Q = 62.8 \text{ k}\Omega,$$

and

$$G = 15.9 \,\mu\text{S}.$$

The minimum value of y_{os} for the transistor is $50 \,\mu\text{S}$.

Thus,

$$y_{os} + G \doteqdot 70 \,\mu\text{S},$$

and

$$M \doteqdot \frac{2 \times 10^{-4} \times 70 \times 10^{-6}}{10^{-3}} = 14 \,\mu\text{H}.$$

If $L_2 = L_1/10$, i.e. approximately 1/3 the number of turns,

$$\sqrt{(L_1 L_2)} = 63 \,\mu\text{H}.$$

The coupling coefficient,

$$k = \frac{M}{\sqrt{(L_1 L_2)}} = 0.22.$$

If the secondary is wound over part of the primary, this coupling can be obtained.

As the reverse biased gate current is small (approximately 10^{-9} A), the gate resistor R_G can be large. A 10-MΩ resistor and 100-pF capacitor ensures a time constant much longer than the period of oscillation. The schematic of the completed design is shown in Fig. 8.10.

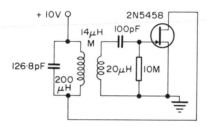

Fig. 8.10. Tuned-drain FET oscillator.

8.6. Colpitts oscillator using a bipolar transistor

In this case the initial divergence of the oscillation is controlled by allowing the collector voltage swing to bottom, i.e. reach the region where the base current curves run together. Also for large signal amplitude, the effective supply voltage can be reached and the swing is limited by cut-off. Both of these effects reduce the current gain but also introduce distortion into the voltage waveforms.

The Colpitts oscillator is convenient because it uses only one inductor which, in combination with C_1 and C_2 of Fig. 8.11, determines the frequency of oscillation. If L is provided with an iron-dust core, this can be adjusted to give the precise frequency of oscillation.

Design considerations

In this example the conditions of oscillation are determined using method (b) of § 8.4. An approximate small signal equivalent network

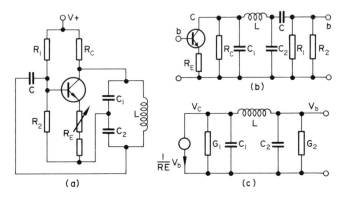

Fig. 8.11. (a) Colpitts oscillator schematic diagram, (b) small-signal diagram and (c) equivalent network, in which the blocking capacitor C has been omitted.

is drawn in Fig. 8.11c, in which G_1 represents the conductance of the collector resistor, and G_2 the effective transistor input conductance in parallel with the bias network. Unlike the previous case for the FET, forward bias must be provided, or oscillations will not start. Because of the unbypassed emitter resistor, R_E, the transistor can be represented by a voltage controlled current source equal to $1/R_E$ with input resistance $h_{fe}R_E$.

Neglecting C_3, a blocking capacitor which isolates the collector direct voltage from the base, and writing the parallel conductance of R_B and R_{in} as G_2 the equations of the network are:

$$\left(G_1 + sC_1 + \frac{1}{sL}\right) v_c - \frac{1}{sL} v_b = -y_f v_b, \qquad (8.15)$$

$$-\frac{1}{sL} v_c + \left(\frac{1}{sL} + sC_2 + G_2\right) v_b = 0, \qquad (8.16)$$

if the currents entering each node are equated to the currents leaving, and $y_f = 1/R_E$.

The determinant of the above equation is

$$s^3 LC_1C_2 + s^2(LC_1G_2 + LC_2G_1) + s(LG_1G_2 + C_1 + C_2) + G_1G_2 + y_f$$
$$= 0.$$

Writing this expression in terms of real frequency (i.e. $s = j\omega$) and equating the imaginary terms to zero,

$$\omega^2 = \frac{[LG_1G_2/(C_1+C_2)]+1}{LC_1C_2/(C_1+C_2)} \div \frac{1}{LC_1C_2/(C_1+C_2)}, \qquad (8.17)$$

$$\left(= \frac{1}{LC/2} \quad \text{if} \quad C_1 = C_2 = C\right).$$

Equating real terms to zero, and substituting for $\omega^2 = (C_1 + C_2)/LC_1C_2$,

$$y_f = \frac{G_1C_2^2 + G_2C_1^2}{C_1C_2}, \qquad (8.18)$$

$$(= G_1 + G_2 \quad \text{if} \quad C_1 = C_2).$$

As R_{in} is much greater than R_B, $G_2 \doteq 1/R_B$.
Thus for the case where $C_1 = C_2$,

$$y_f = \frac{1}{R_E} \doteq \frac{1}{R_C} + \frac{1}{R_B},$$

or

$$R_E = \frac{R_B R_C}{R_B + R_C}. \qquad (8.19)$$

Choice of transistor. The main consideration is the cut-off frequency of the transistor. Commonly, r.f. transistors are used in fixed frequency oscillators up to 1.25 times the cut-off frequency, while in variable frequency oscillators the limit is usually about 0.8 times f_α.

Design steps
    1. Using the expression (8.17) select values for L, C_1 and C_2 to obtain the desired frequency of oscillation. If the two capacitors are equal, the necessary gain adjustment can be accomplished with R_E.
    2. Choose R_1 and R_2 to give a suitable emitter voltage for R_E, to determine the standing collector current.
    3. Select a value of R_C which will provide a satisfactory collector voltage swing.
    4. Calculate the appropriate value of R_E required for oscillation.

DESIGN EXAMPLE 8.2

Required, a Colpitts oscillator operating at 500 kHz, using a BC108 transistor. A power supply of 10 V is available.

The tuned circuit. To obtain frequency stability independent of the collector capacitance the tuned circuit capacitors should be relatively large. Let $C_1 = C_2 = 500$ pF.

From eqn. (8.17)

$$L = 2/\omega^2 C, \quad \text{where} \quad \omega = 2\pi f,$$
$$= 100 \ \mu\text{H}.$$

D.C. biasing. Assuming a collector current of 1.5 mA, the collector voltage will be approximately 6 V if R_C is 2.7 kΩ. If R_B is assumed to be 2 kΩ, the requirement for oscillation

$$R_E = \frac{R_B R_C}{R_B + R_C} = \frac{2 \text{ k}\Omega \times 2.7 \text{ k}\Omega}{2 \text{ k}\Omega + 2.7 \text{ k}\Omega} = 1.15 \text{ k}\Omega.$$

If R_E is made up from a 560 Ω fixed resistor, and a 1 kΩ variable resistance, it can be adjusted to give the correct value of oscillation. Assuming a nominal value of 1 kΩ for R_E, the necessary base voltage for a collector current of 1.5 mA is

$$V_B = I_E R_E + V_{BE} = 1.5 \text{ V} + 0.6 \text{ V} \doteqdot 2 \text{ V}.$$

Suitable values for R_1 and R_2 are 10 kΩ and 2.2 kΩ which give a nominal value of 1.8 kΩ for R_B, and a V_B of 1.8 V. Because of additional losses, such as inductor resistance, the value for R_E will be somewhat lower than that calculated, and the design collector current will be obtained with these values.

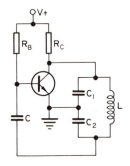

Fig. 8.12. Colpitts oscillator with base current bias.

As there is a high degree of negative feedback, the condition for oscillation does not depend directly on the transistor parameters, and most transistors will perform satisfactorily in this configuration.

Figure 8.12 shows how self-bias could be used with this oscillator. Although simpler, there is little control over the operating conditions and C_1 and C_2 will usually require adjustment for satisfactory operation.

Field effect transistor Colpitts oscillator. Figure 8.13 shows a form of the Colpitts oscillator using a FET with gate self-bias. As

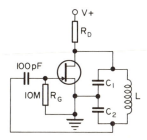

Fig. 8.13. FET Colpitts oscillator with gate self-bias. A better waveform is obtained if R_D is replaced by an inductor.

shown in the equivalent diagram, the conditions of oscillation are similar to those in the previous example, except that G_2 can be considered as zero.

For oscillation

$$y_{fs} = G_1.$$

Most devices will meet this requirement and will oscillate in this configuration. The negative gate voltage will build up, reducing y_{fs} to a value that will maintain constant oscillation. Usually a better waveform can be obtained if R_D is replaced by a choke which is an inductor of about 20 mH.

8.7. Resistance–capacitance oscillators

Due to the convenience of resistors and capacitors compared with inductors, and also due to their lower cost, RC oscillators are preferred for operation up to 10 MHz.

Two common forms of RC oscillator are:

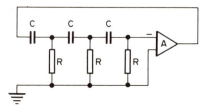

Fig. 8.14. Phase shift oscillator. The $C-R$ network provides a phase shift of 180° at the frequency of oscillation, and the necessary amplifier gain is -29.

(a) *Phase shift.* This type of oscillator is illustrated in Fig. 8.14. For this network, when the amplifier has infinite input resistance, zero output resistance, and equal capacitors and resistors, the condition for maintenance of oscillation is that the gain should be -29. This is the gain necessary to compensate for the attenuation of the phase-shifting network. The latter has a phase angle, at the frequency of oscillation, of 180° and the amplifier is required to have signal inversion to make the overall phase shift around the feedback loop zero. The frequency of oscillation is

$$f = \frac{1}{2\pi RC\sqrt{6}}. \tag{8.20}$$

(b) *Wien bridge type.* The reactive part of a Wien bridge forms a transmission network with zero phase shift at one frequency. When combined with an amplifier with no signal inversion an oscillating system can be formed.

8.8.   Wien bridge oscillator

The Wien bridge oscillator is widely used as a variable frequency oscillator in the frequency range from 1 to 10^7 Hz, and provides a range of frequency variation which is greater than can be obtained from LC systems. The frequency can be controlled by ganged variable resistors as in Fig. 8.16.

Design considerations

Figure 8.15 illustrates the basic arrangement. If the feedback network is regarded as a voltage divider, its transfer function is

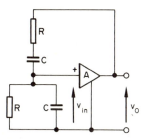

Fig. 8.15. Wien bridge oscillator. The C–R network provides zero phase shift at the frequency of oscillation, and the necessary amplifier gain is 3.

$$\frac{v_0}{v_{in}} = \frac{\dfrac{R}{1+sCR}}{\dfrac{R}{1+sCR}+\dfrac{1+sCR}{sC}},$$

$$= \frac{sCR}{1+3sCR+(sCR)^2},$$

$$= \frac{s\tau}{1+3s\tau+(s\tau)^2}, \quad \text{writing} \quad \tau = CR. \qquad (8.21)$$

The condition for oscillation is that the gain around the feedback loop should be unity, i.e. $A\beta = 1$, where A is the amplifier gain.

After substituting $j\omega = s$,

$$\frac{Aj\omega\tau}{1+3j\omega\tau+(j\omega\tau)^2} = 1. \qquad (8.22)$$

Rearranging,

$$\omega^2\tau^2+(A-3)j\omega\tau-1 = 0$$

and equating imaginary terms to zero,

$$A = 3. \qquad (8.23)$$

Equating real terms to zero,

$$\omega = \frac{1}{\tau} = \frac{1}{CR}. \qquad (8.24)$$

Thus if the amplifier has zero phase shift, infinite input resistance and zero output resistance, it is required to have a gain of 3, and the frequency of oscillation is given by $\omega = 1/CR$. Since LC oscillators have their frequency inversely proportional to the square root of LC, the Wien bridge arrangement can obviously provide a wider frequency range, and this is one reason why it is preferred for use in laboratory-type instruments. By using a ganged variable resistor, a 10 to 1 variation in frequency is readily obtained. In practice it is difficult to obtain perfect matching of the resistors over the complete range, and the amplifier will have a finite output impedance. In addition, the gain of the amplifier is likely to vary with frequency, so that it is probable that at some point in the tuning range the conditions for the maintenance of oscillations will not be met. To ensure that this does not happen, causing oscillations to cease, a non-linear element is usually included in the circuit, acting in such a manner that the gain of the amplifier is kept at a suitable level.

Design steps
1. Design an amplifier system which has a gain of 3, without signal inversion.
2. From eqn. (8.24) calculate values of C and R to obtain the correct frequency or range of frequencies.
3. Provide some non-linear element to stabilize the amplifier gain and thus maintain the conditions required for oscillation.

DESIGN EXAMPLE 8.3
Required a modified Wien bridge oscillator covering the frequency range 1 to 10 kHz.
The amplifier. The simplest arrangement is the series–parallel feedback system, using an operational amplifier (see § 6.3.8). As

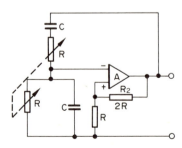

Fig. 8.16. Series–parallel connection for the amplifier of the Wien oscillator.

shown in Fig. 8.16, if $R_2 = 2R$ the gain, which is the reciprocal of the feedback ratio β, is 3. The system thus acts as a voltage amplifier with a high input resistance, low output resistance, and a voltage gain of $+3$. A general-purpose operational amplifier, such as the 741, will have adequate bandwidth for this purpose, since the closed-loop bandwidth will be 1/3 of the unity gain value, and will be approximately 300 kHz.

Frequency. Let the selected ganged potentiometer have a maximum value of 50 kΩ. The maximum value of R will yield the lowest frequency, 1 kHz. Thus, $C = 1/\omega R = 3184$ pF; 3300 pF would be a suitable value.

Gain stabilization. For the amplitude of oscillation to be maintained constant over the range of operation, automatic adjustment for variations in the oscillation maintenance conditions is necessary. This can be accomplished, as in Fig. 8.17, by the use of a thermistor, a device with a high negative temperature coefficient of resistance.

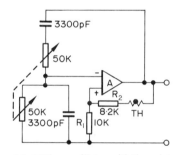

Fig. 8.17. Completed Wien oscillator with thermistor stabilization.

If the signal level falls, its resistance increases and the feedback fraction is reduced. This increases the amplifier gain, which restores the original signal level. A thermistor which has a cold resistance of about 10 kΩ would operate satisfactorily with R_1 and R_2.

8.9. Closed-loop level control

An alternative gain stabilization system is shown in Fig. 8.18. A field effect transistor is used as a variable resistor element. The output waveform is rectified and smoothed to provide a negative voltage proportional to the amplitude of oscillation. At switch-on,

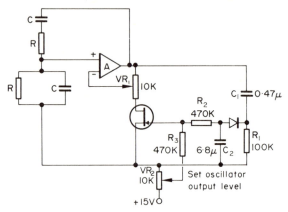

Fig. 8.18. Use of a FET as a variable resistor to control oscillator output level.

the control voltage is zero and FET channel resistance is at its minimum value, thereby providing a small feedback fraction and consequently high gain. The oscillation amplitude will build up until the peak voltage is equal to the voltage set on VR_2. The feedback resistance control VR_1 is adjusted to the maximum value which allows oscillation. This ensures that the FET has the minimum voltage across it, thus ensuring that the range of drain–source voltage, over which the device performs as a linear resistor, is not exceeded. (In Fig. 8.18 this is somewhat less than 1 V.) In this way a full range of output voltage is possible up to the saturation level of the amplifier.

Design considerations
C_1 and R_1 are selected so that the oscillation frequency will be passed without appreciable phase shift or attenuation, i.e.

$$C_1 R_1 \geqslant 10/2\pi f,$$

where f is the lowest frequency of oscillation.

R_2 is equal to R_3 ensuring that the negative peak oscillator voltage is compared with V_R and adjusts to this value by either increasing or decreasing the FET resistance. The change in gate voltage is very small over the full range of oscillator amplitude. The actual oscillator voltage will be higher than the reference voltage because of the forward voltage across the diode.

C_2 should be sufficiently large to ensure that the voltage developed across it does not change during the oscillation cycle.

More precise operation can be obtained if a non-inverting voltage amplifier is placed between the comparison resistors and the FET gate. A nominal gain of 10 increases the gain around the control loop, reducing response times. A 10-kΩ resistor between the output and gate ensures that, if the gate is positive, the current is limited.

8.10. Frequency stability

If the loop gain, $A\beta$, of an oscillator is unity, the frequency of oscillation will be that at which the phase shift around the loop is zero. Should there by any change in the phase angle of A, the frequency of oscillation will automatically take up a new value at which the loop phase angle is zero. Consequently, for good frequency stability a network should be used which, for a small change in frequency, provides a large change in phase angle. A resonant L–C circuit has this property, which improves as Q is increased. Figure 8.19 represents the equivalent network of a quartz crystal,

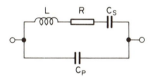

Fig. 8.19. Equivalent network of a quartz crystal.

and such a device might typically have a Q 1000 times greater than an L–C tuned circuit operating under the same conditions. It is for this reason that quartz crystals are used where a fixed frequency is required with very good frequency stability.

Simple form of crystal-controlled oscillator

The oscillator shown in Fig. 8.20 provides a feedback path from drain to gate, through the crystal which controls the frequency of oscillation. The arrangement, sometimes known as the *Pierce oscillator,* can be regarded as a modification of the Colpitts form.

The design steps are straightforward.

1. Obtain a crystal of the required frequency.

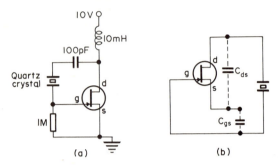

Fig. 8.20. (a) A simple form of crystal oscillator. The gate waveform is usually less distorted than that of the drain. (b) Small-signal diagram showing the similarity with the Colpitts oscillator. The inductor isolates the drain from the + 10 V for high frequencies.

2.   Select the gate-leak components. For a FET, since the gate current is very small, a large value of resistance can be used, 1 to 10 MΩ usually being satisfactory. For operating frequencies in the region of 1 MHz a value of $C = 100 \, \text{pF}$ is appropriate. If "squegging" (i.e. bursts of oscillation) occurs, the CR time constant should be reduced.

3.   The drain current will automatically set to the appropriate value to maintain oscillation because of the negative self-bias generated by the gate current. However, the maximum current, and the highest y_{fs}, is set by the current at zero gate-source voltage. An inductor drain load, because of its low resistance, will usually ensure that the system will oscillate. If a resistive load is used, and the supply voltage is a nominal 10 V, a value of 1 kΩ could be necessary to allow sufficient drain current.

8.11.   The series resonant oscillator

A crystal, as represented by Fig. 8.19, has two main resonant frequencies.
   (a) Series resonance with L and C_s.
   (b) Parallel resonance with L and C_p.
For maximum stability the series resonant condition is preferred both for crystal and L–C circuits. This is because at series resonance the circuit has low impedance and is consequently less

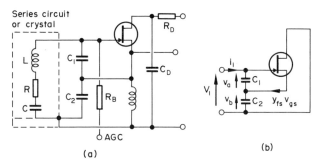

Fig. 8.21. (a) Series-resonant oscillator. C_1 and C_2 should be large enough to mask device capacitances. The output is taken from the source. (b) Small-signal network used to calculate the amplifier negative resistance.

affected by external loading than is the high impedance parallel circuit. In the network of Fig. 8.21a representing a series resonant oscillator, the frequency determining elements may be either a series tuned circuit or a crystal, although not all crystals will operate in the series mode. The impedance seen by the series network can be determined by finding an expression for the input voltage using Fig. 8.21b.

$$v_1 = v_a + v_b,$$

where v_a is the voltage across C_1, and is the gate-source voltage v_{gs}. The voltage v_b is developed by the current $i_i + i_d$ flowing through C_2, $(i_d = y_{fs}v_{gs})$.

Thus,

$$v_1 = \frac{i_1}{sC_1} + \frac{i_1 + y_{fs}v_a}{sC_2},$$

$$= \left(\frac{1}{sC_1} + \frac{1}{sC_2} + \frac{y_{fs}}{s^2C_1C_2}\right)i_1. \tag{8.25}$$

The input impedance,

$$Z_{in}(s) = \frac{v_1}{i_1} = \frac{1}{sC_1} + \frac{1}{sC_2} + \frac{y_{fs}}{s^2C_1C_2},$$

or

$$Z_{in}(j\omega) = \frac{1}{j\omega C_1} + \frac{1}{j\omega C_2} - \frac{y_{fs}}{\omega^2C_1C_2}. \tag{8.26}$$

The third term represents a negative resistance and, as established in § 8.1, for oscillations to build up this must be greater than R, the series resistance of the tuned circuit or crystal. The condition for maintenance of a constant amplitude of oscillation is that the negative resistance should be equal to R. The series impedance of the tuned circuit of Fig. 8.21a is

$$Z(j\omega) = j\omega L + \frac{1}{j\omega C} + R + Z_{in}(j\omega), \quad \text{and using eqn. (9.26)},$$

$$= \left(1 - \omega^2 LC + j\omega CR + \frac{C}{C_1} + \frac{C}{C_2} - \frac{jy_{fs}C}{\omega C_1 C_2}\right)\frac{1}{j\omega C}. \quad (8.27)$$

For oscillation, this impedance must be zero. Equating real and imaginary parts of eqn. (8.27) to zero,

$$\omega^2 = \frac{1}{LC}\left(1 + \frac{C}{C_1} + \frac{C}{C_2}\right), \quad \text{and} \quad R = \frac{y_{fs}}{\omega^2 C_1 C_2}. \quad (8.28)$$

Design steps

1. From the Q of the inductor, determine the series resistance.

2. Assuming a value for y_{fs} and using eqn. (8.28), calculate the product $C_1 C_2$ and determine the required values assuming $C_1 = C_2$. (It is desirable that these values should be large as they will mask changes in network capacitances.)

3. Calculate the required tuning capacitance.

4. Set up the bias network. In the simplest case this could be a gate resistor. For good frequency stability use automatic gain control (AGC).

DESIGN EXAMPLE 8.4

Required, a series resonant oscillator operating at 1 MHz. Assuming the inductor is 500 μH and has a Q at 1 MHz of 110, from the expression $Q = \omega L/R$, the effective series resistance is

$$R = \frac{\omega L}{Q} = \frac{2\pi \times 10^6 \times 500 \times 10^{-6}}{110} = 28.5 \ \Omega.$$

If a FET with a minimum value of $y_{fs} = 1.5$ mS is to be used, from eqn. (8.28),

$$C_1 C_2 = \frac{y_{fs}}{\omega^2 R} = \frac{1.5 \times 10^{-3}}{(2\pi)^2 \times 10^{12} \times 28.5} = 1.33 \times 10^{-18} \text{ F}^2.$$

Assuming equal values,

$$C_1 = C_2 = 1000 \text{ pF} \quad \text{will ensure oscillation.}$$

Tuning capacitor. The nominal value for

$$C = \frac{1}{(2\pi)^2 L f} = 50.7 \text{ pF}.$$

From the expression for resonance it is apparent that this value is reduced by 10 per cent because of the effects of C_1 and C_2. A 47-pF capacitor is satisfactory, if there is some means of frequency adjustment such as a trimming capacitor or tuning slug on the inductor.

Bias network. A 1-MΩ gate resistor will provide the necessary bias, but this operation depends on the gate voltage going positive and allowing current to flow into the gate. This inevitably introduces distortion into the waveform causing the generation of frequencies other than the fundamental. An automatic gain control, as shown in Fig. 8.22, will enable the level of oscillation to be maintained constant at a gate voltage which does not require current to flow. This is accomplished by rectifying the output and comparing it with the reference voltage. The difference is amplified and used as the

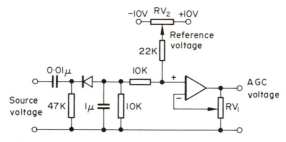

Fig. 8.22. Rectifier and amplifier of the automatic level control. The gate resistor (R_B in Fig. 8.21) should be about 47 kΩ rather than the somewhat higher value for a self-bias system.

negative gate bias. The amplifier gain should be set to as high a value as possible, which permits stable operation. The level can then be set to an appropriate value which does not allow the gate voltage to go positive.

Source inductor. The inductance should be such that at the operating frequency the impedance is much greater than that of C_2. A value of 10 mH is satisfactory.

CHAPTER 9

Waveform Generators

INTRODUCTION

When the loop gain of an oscillator is very much greater than unity, the output waveform is not sinusoidal, but varies between two limits. Such non-linear oscillations have been examined by Van der Pol[48] and are known as relaxation oscillators.

The most important class of relaxation oscillators is the multivibrator family which may be divided into three main groups as follows:

(a) Astable multivibrators (AMV) having no stable state.
(b) Monostable multivibrators (MMV or flip-flop), having one stable state.
(c) Bistable multivibrators (BMV or binary), having two stable states.

Each of these types can be considered as a two-stage amplifier with output connected to input, as shown in the circuit diagram of Fig. 9.1.

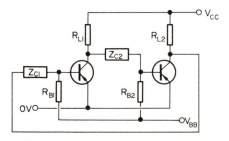

Fig. 9.1. Two-stage amplifier with output connected to input, thus forming a positive feedback system. The form of the coupling impedances, Z_{C1} and Z_{C2} determine the class of multivibrator.

353

9.1. Multivibrators—General survey of the three types

AMV

If the coupling impedances Z_{c1} and Z_{c2} are capacitors and $V_{BB} = 0$ the device is an astable multivibrator. Because of the a.c. coupling it has no stable state and will provide an output voltage of rectangular form, the duration of which is controlled by the time constants of the base circuits.[49] Applications of the AMV include:[50]

(a) *Timing oscillator.* The symmetrical AMV can be used as a "clock generator" producing X and Y pulses, each collector providing one output (see Fig. 9.2).

(b) *Variable-frequency oscillator.* The frequency of oscillation may be controlled electronically by varying V_{BB} or mechanically, by changing component values in the base network.

(c) *Frequency divider.* The AMV can be readily synchronized to an input signal and used for counting down.

(d) *Harmonic generation.* Because of the rapid transitions of the waveform high-order harmonics are generated.

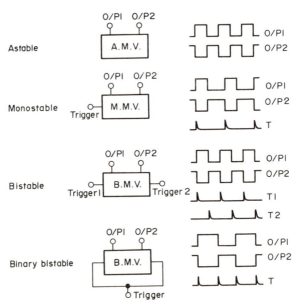

Fig. 9.2. Basic types of multivibrator.

BMV

If the coupling impedances of Fig. 9.1 are resistive and the value of V_{BB} is such that either transistor may be held cut-off, the bistable conditions can be obtained.[51] It can be arranged that either transistor is conducting, holding the other transistor beyond cut-off, and such a stable state can be maintained indefinitely. To change the state of the device a trigger signal must be introduced. The BMV is the most widely used type of multivibrator, and among its many applications there are:[52]

(a) *Counting.* As two successive input signals are necessary to restore the circuit to its original state, it may be used for counting by two.

(b) *Memory element.* The two alternative states of the BMV may be designated "no" (or "0") and "yes" (or "1") and this facility is used in shift register circuits.

MMV

If one coupling impedance is resistive and the other is capacitive the device will have one stable state. The transistor with capacitive coupling is held "on", while the other transistor is held "off" by the resistive coupling and V_{BB}. When triggered, a single output pulse is obtained, of duration determined by the base time constant. The MMV is commonly used for:

(a) *Pulse forming.* An input pulse can be transformed into a pulse of controlled duration and amplitude.

(b) *Counting.* The MMV having once been triggered, is insensitive to further trigger pulses until it reverts to its former state. This property makes the device useful as a counter.

(c) *Delay.* The trailing edge of the output waveform may be used to provide a pulse delayed from the input pulse. Since the duration of the output waveform may be controlled, as in the AMV, a variable delay is obtainable.

9.2. Transistor switching[53]

Direct coupling

In Fig. 9.3a T_1 and T_2 are transistors having the typical characteristics of Fig. 9.3b. When T_1 is conducting T_2 is "off", because the bottoming voltage of T_1 is less than the conducting voltage of T_2.

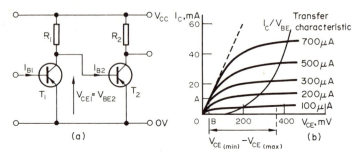

Fig. 9.3. Direct coupled transistors. When T_1 is conducting T_2 is off and vice versa.

If the base of T_1 is supplied with a base current of 1 mA, and if $V_{CC}/R_1 = 10$ mA, then T_1 will bottom at approximately 30 mV, which is less than the conducting value of V_{BE} for T_2. If I_{B1} becomes zero, the collector voltage of T_1 will try to approach V_{CC}, but the base of T_2 will hold the voltage to approximately 0.4 V. The major part of the current previously flowing into the collector of T_1 will now be flowing into the base of T_2. Thus, although there is a transfer of current from T_1 to T_2, the voltage at the collector of T_1 changes by less than 0.4 V. This has been considered previously with respect to direct coupled amplifiers. The waveforms obtained are shown in Fig. 9.4.

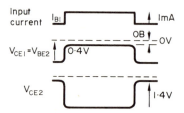

Fig. 9.4. Switching waveforms obtained from the transistors arranged as in Fig. 9.3.

Resistor coupling

If a greater collector voltage swing is required, than is possible with direct coupling, the collector of T_1 may be connected to the base of T_2 by a resistor. This reduces the base current I_{B2} to a value that is sufficient to switch T_2, but does not cause excessive voltage drop in R_1. Thus, if V_{BE2} and $I_{B2} \cdot R_1$ are neglected,

$$I_{B2} \doteqdot V_{CC}/R_B \quad \text{(see Fig. 9.5).} \tag{9.1}$$

Normally, R_B is selected such that the transistor will just bottom.

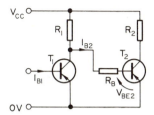

Fig. 9.5. Use of coupling resistor to allow a greater voltage swing at the collector of the first transistor.

This gives a defined switching level of the order of 50 mV and ensures low power dissipation in the device. Referring to the characteristic curves of Fig. 9.6, if R_C is 1 kΩ the drive current required to bottom the transistor is approximately 120 μA. The value of base current required is a function of the collector current. If a larger collector resistor is used, the base current necessary for bottoming will be reduced.

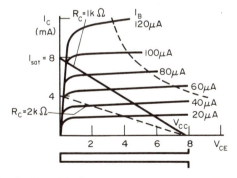

Fig. 9.6. Determination of the base current necessary to turn a transistor "on".

Saturated operation

The maximum current that can flow in the collector is the saturation current, and this occurs when V_{CE} is a minimum ($\doteqdot 0$ V).

Thus, $I_{sat} = V_{CC}/R_C$. For saturated operation, the limits of the output waveform are:

$$(V_{CE} \doteq 0 \text{ V}, I_C = I_{sat}) \quad \text{and} \quad (V_{CE} \doteq V_{CC}, I_C = I_{CEO} \doteq 0).$$

Power dissipation, $P_C = I_C V_{CE}$ is small in either condition.

$$\text{Collector current} \quad I_C = I_{CEO} + h_{FE} \cdot I_B, \tag{9.2}$$

where h_{FE} is the large signal s/c current gain. Thus, $I_B = I_{sat}/h_{FE}$ gives the required value of base current for saturation. To ensure that saturation is attained the minimum value of h_{FE} should be used.

9.3.   Speed of transistor switching[54]

When a transistor is switched on, for saturated operation it must pass through three different conditions:

   (a) Transistor "off". The base–emitter junction is reverse biased and only leakage current flows in the collector circuit. $I_C = I_{CEO}$.
   (b) Transistor in active region of operation. $I_C = I_{CEO} + h_{FE} \cdot I_B$.
   (c) Transistor in saturated condition. $I_C = I_{sat}$.

When the transistor is switched off the sequence is reversed, and the time taken to pass through these three conditions is the switching time.

The switching-on sequence requires that a charge be put into the base, while when switching off the charge must be removed, and the speed of operation is related to the time required to accomplish this. The increase in base current to provide such a charge, above that

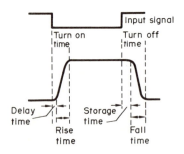

Fig. 9.7. Transistor switching sequence for a rectangular pulse input.

necessary for saturation, is called the *overdrive* current. Overdrive will decrease the turn-on time, but in general, will increase the turn-off time because of carrier storage. The use of overdrive makes provision for the spread in characteristics and ensures that transistors with the lowest current gain are bottomed.

To assist in charging and discharging the base, it is usual to shunt the coupling resistor with a *speed-up* capacitor. This should be large enough to supply the required charge, but not so large as to slow down the switching time by requiring a large recharging period.

9.4. Bistable multivibrator

Figure 9.8 represents the basic arrangement of a symmetrical, collector-to-base coupled circuit. It is required that, as a stable condition, when T_1 is conducting T_2 should be cut off. Since the

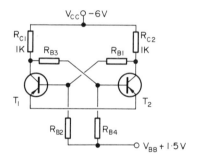

Fig. 9.8. Basic arrangement of a symmetrical collector-to-base coupled circuit.

transistors shown are *pnp*, the application of a positive trigger pulse to the base of T_1 drives it to cut off, and the resulting negative voltage transmitted from its collector to the base of T_2 causes that transistor to conduct. This state (T_2 conducting and T_1 cut-off) is maintained until another trigger pulse is applied to the base of T_2.

Design considerations

The choice of component values is to some extent a matter of compromise. Since the transistors are saturated when "on", the amplitude of the output voltage waveform is independent of the value of the collector resistor. The selection of this resistor is therefore a compromise between economy of current and speed of operation.

The speed-up capacitors are not essential for operation of the circuit, but should be used where small rise times are required. They should be chosen such that, with the coupling resistors, they form time constants equal to the transistor input circuit time constant, $r_{b'e} \cdot C_{in}$. A capacitor greater than this will decrease the rise time further, but tend to give an overshoot.

The use of a positive base supply V_{BB} reduces the switching time out of the saturation condition. If the bias chain is of much greater resistance than the collector resistor, the collector voltage may be considered as being either at V_{CC} or at 0 V, depending on whether the transistor is "off" or "on". Thus when T_1 is conducting, $V_{CI} \doteqdot 0$, and the base voltage of T_2,

$$V_{B2} = V_{BB} \frac{R_4}{(R_3 + R_4)}, \tag{9.3}$$

which should be sufficient to hold T_2 cut-off. When T_1 is cut-off, $V_{CI} \doteqdot V_{CC}$ and V_{B2} will be approximately -0.3 V, causing T_2 to conduct.

Choice of transistor

This is largely determined by the required speed of operation; if f_1 is the cut-off frequency of the transistor, then a speed of operation of the order of $f_1/10$ is possible.

Design steps

1. Select values for the collector resistors, to provide the required saturation current.
2. Construct a load line on the characteristic curves, and determine the base current for saturation. Allow for 100 per cent overdrive.
3. Calculate values for the coupling and bias resistors, and choose a suitable speed-up capacitor.

DESIGN EXAMPLE 9.1

Required, a bistable multivibrator capable of operation up to 250 kHz. A suitable transistor is the 2G 301 having a cut-off frequency of 3–6 MHz. Let V_{CC} be -6 V and $V_{BB} = +1.5$ V.

Make $R_{C1} = R_{C2} = 1\,k\Omega$ giving a saturation current of $V_{CC}/R_C = 6\,mA$. If the load line is drawn in Fig. 9.6 it will be seen that a base current I_B of $100\,\mu A$ is required for saturation. Let the design figure be $200\,\mu A$ to allow for transistors having low current gain (100 per cent overdrive).

Bias resistors. The positive bias supply must provide the leakage current $I_{CB0(max)}$ ($= 60\,\mu A$ from the manufacturer's data). Thus,

$$R_{B2} = R_{B4} = \frac{V_{BB}}{I_{CB0(max)}} = \frac{1.5\,V}{60\,\mu A} = 25\,k\Omega.$$

Let them have the preferred value of $22\,k\Omega$.

Coupling resistors. When the base is forward biased, R_{B4} passes current:

$$I_1 = 0.08\,mA \quad (\text{see Fig. 9.9}).$$

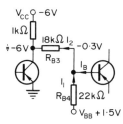

Fig. 9.9. Calculation of coupling resistance for Design Example 9.1.

But

$$I_2 = I_B + I_1 = 0.28\,mA.$$

Therefore,

$$R_{B3} = \frac{V_{CC}}{I_2} = \frac{6\,V}{0.28\,mA} \doteqdot 21\,k\Omega.$$

This is a maximum value for R_{B1} and R_{B3} which may, with advantage, be reduced to accommodate variations in voltage supply and resistor tolerances. Let the design value be $18\,k\Omega$.

Speed-up capacitors. The optimum value for speed-up capacitors can be calculated, but for the transistors chosen a value of $470\,pF$ is indicated.

In Fig. 9.10 the completed circuit is drawn together with a suitable triggering arrangement.

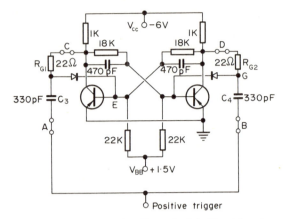

Fig. 9.10. Completed circuit of Design Example 9.1. The triggering arrangement provides binary operation.

9.5.   Triggering

To change the bistable from one state to the other, diode gating is usually employed. The "on" transistor forward biases the diode connected to its base, while the "off" transistor reverse biases its base diode. The former base will thus accept a positive pulse which switches it off and changes the state of the circuit.

In some applications, shift registers for instance, gating is controlled from another stage in which case the network is opened at C and D. Other applications require two channels for input pulses. If the network is opened at A and B, only the first pulse of a series on one channel will switch the device, unless the other channel is triggered. A series of waveforms obtained when the circuit is operated as a binary counter is drawn in Fig. 9.11a.

Input capacitors C_3 and C_4

These are required to switch off a transistor with a positive going trigger pulse. The selection of values is a compromise between ensuring operation and avoiding limitation of the repetition rate. They should be large enough to remove the base charge in the switching-off sequence but not so large that they are unable to discharge sufficiently before the arrival of the next triggering pulse.

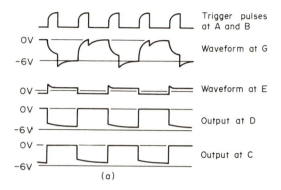

(a)

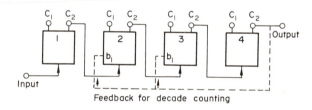

Feedback for decade counting

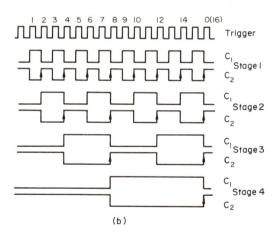

(b)

Fig. 9.11. (a) Waveforms obtained when the circuit of Fig. 9.10 is operated as a binary element. (b) Connection of binary elements to form a four-stage counter. This is basically a binary counter but application of feedback as shown transforms it into a decade counter.

364   ELECTRONICS FROM THEORY INTO PRACTICE

9.6.   Alternative gating methods

Collector triggering

Referring to Fig. 9.12, with T_1 conducting, D_1 is reverse biased.
Trigger pulses are therefore routed to the collector of T_2 and from
there to the base of T_1 via the cross-coupling network. This method
has the advantage of only requiring one input capacitor, but a larger
trigger pulse is necessary.

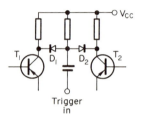

Fig. 9.12. Collector triggering for binary operation.

Collector triggering using a transistor

This method is frequently used for (*DCTL*) direct-coupled logic
circuits, and has the basic arrangement of Fig. 9.13. A negative
voltage applied to the base of T_3 or T_4 will switch on the non-
conducting transistor of the BMV. It will not, however, have any
effect on the conducting transistor. The circuit may be modified to
that of Fig. 9.14. Assume an initial condition of T_1 conducting and T_2
"off". Since T_5 is normally non-conducting, C_1 will only be charged
to the bottoming voltage, but C_2 will be charged to the
maximum collector voltage of -0.4 V. The application of a trigger to
the base of T_5, causing it to conduct, effectively connects the
emitters of T_3 and T_4 to 0 V. Thus the voltage on C_2 is applied
between base and emitter of T_4, causing it to conduct; this in turn
switches off T_1 (and switches on T_2).

9.7.   Emitter-coupled BMV

The positive base bias supply may be obtained by using a common
emitter resistor, bypassed by a capacitor for high-frequency currents, as shown in Fig. 9.15. To maintain the same conditions as in

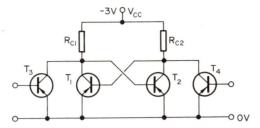

Fig. 9.13. Collector triggering using transistors. The trigger transistors are T_3 and T_4.

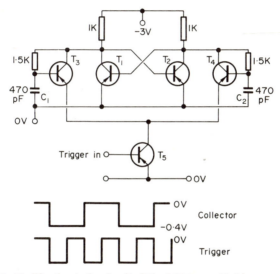

Fig. 9.14. Modification to the circuit of Fig. 9.13 to provide binary operation.

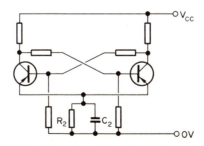

Fig. 9.15. Provision of base bias using emitter resistor R_2.

the previous example, V_{CC} is increased from -6 to $-7.5V$. As the collector current is 6 mA,

$$R_E = \frac{V_{BB}}{I_E} = \frac{1.5\ V}{6\ mA} = 250\ \Omega.$$

The switching time is of the order of 1 μs, and the time constant $C_E R_E$ should be made at least 10 times greater than this. Let $C_E R_E = 10\ \mu$s. Then

$$C_E = 10^{-5}/250 = 4 \times 10^{-9}.\quad \text{Let it be } 0.047\ \mu F.$$

If the emitter resistor is not bypassed, emitter coupling can be used and one of the collector-to-base coupling networks removed. The circuit then becomes that of Fig. 9.16. The regenerative loop then consists of a common collector stage driving a common base stage, which is coupled back to the former by R_{B3} and R_{B4}. The collector of T_2 is "free" since it does not enter directly into the feedback loop, and R_{C2} can have any value less than R_{C1}.

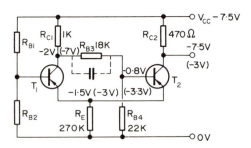

Fig. 9.16. Emitter-coupled multivibrator. The voltages in brackets refer to the condition of T_2 conducting.

When T_1 is "on", T_2 is "off", because its base is positive with respect to the emitter voltage. When T_2 conducts it draws an increased current through R_E cutting off T_1. The base voltage of T_1 will become more negative when T_1 is "off", because it will only be drawing leakage current. If it becomes -2 V, then its emitter should be approximately -3 V, to ensure that the emitter–base junction is reversed biased. Thus,

$$I_{E2} = \frac{V_E}{R_E} = \frac{3\ V}{270} \doteq 10\ mA.$$

With $R_{C2} = 470\,\Omega$, the output voltage will vary between -7.5 and -3 V. Such an arrangement has a loop gain less than unity at zero frequency and will not switch from one state to another. It will, in fact, perform as an amplifier with the output limiting at -7.5 V (cut-off) or -3 V (conducting).

If C is made sufficiently large, the circuit will have a gain which is greater than unity at high frequency, and will be switched by relatively fast moving waveforms. The gain may also be increased by the use of a larger R_{C1} or R_E. If C is made $0.01\,\mu$F the device will perform effectively as a trigger circuit. Typical waveforms for the "switching" and "non-switching" states of this circuit are given in Fig. 9.17.

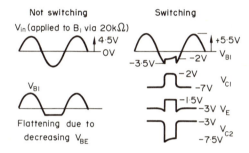

Fig. 9.17. Typical waveforms for the circuit of Fig. 9.16.

9.8. Symmetrical trigger BMV

The symmetrical BMV can also be used as a trigger device. To switch a transistor "on", the input voltage must be raised to a value that will produce conduction, and the reverse process is required for switching the transistor "off". The circuit of Fig. 9.18a can be

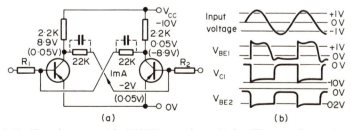

Fig. 9.18. Use of a symmetrical BMV as a trigger device. The waveforms show the circuit being used to square a sine wave input.

triggered by the appropriate voltage at either base, i.e. -0.3 V to bring a *pnp* transistor on, and 0 V to switch off. The waveforms obtained with a sinusoidal input are given in Fig. 9.18b.

9.9. Complementary bistable networks

If the *npn* and *pnp* transistors of Fig. 9.19 are biased correctly, the combination will have a current gain greater than unity with no signal inversion. It therefore has properties similar to a point contact

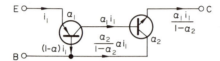

Fig. 9.19. Complementary pair to provide current gain without signal inversion.

transistor, and is able to exhibit a negative resistance characteristic across its input terminals. The combination may be used in the form of Fig. 9.20. When T_1 is "off", $V_{C1} = -V$ and V_{BE2} is too small to turn T_2 "on". Both transistors are therefore "off". With T_1 "on", $V_{C1} \doteqdot + V$ and transistor T_2 also conducts.

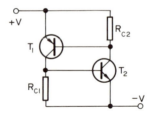

Fig. 9.20. Coupling of complementary device to provide a regenerative loop.

A circuit employing this combination of transistors is given in Fig. 9.21. When the input voltage exceeds the reference voltage V_R, both transistors are switched on regeneratively. The emitter resistor R_E draws current and V_{E1} falls to approximately 3 V. A further fall in V_{E1} will cause T_1 to start cutting off, which regeneratively switches off both transistors.

With such a network, a relatively large current pulse can be obtained from the emitter of T_2. Since the input circuit demands an

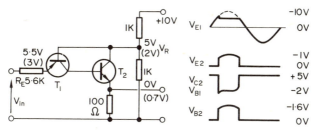

Fig. 9.21. Complementary bistable network. A square wave output is obtained from a sinusoidal input.

increasing current as the voltage falls, it exhibits negative resistance. The use of too large a value for R_E can reduce the gain so much that the network will not switch.

9.10. Integrated circuit bistables

The simplest form of bistable element is a latching circuit, but its field of application is restricted. The two devices which have found widest use are the type D edge triggered, and the type JK master–slave flip-flops, exemplified by the SN 7474 and SN 7476 respectively.

R–S latch

A simple latching circuit can be made with two *NAND* gates connected as in Fig. 9.22. For a NAND gate, the output is at logic "0" (low) only if all its inputs are at logic "1" (high). If any one input is low then the output is high.

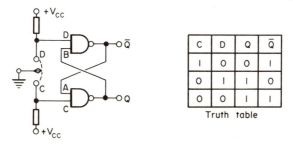

C	D	Q	Q̄
I	0	0	I
0	I	I	0
0	0	I	I

Truth table

Fig. 9.22. *R–S* latch made up of two NAND gates.

The arrangement shown enables a clean switching action to be obtained from a mechanical switch subject to contact bounce. Thus if the switch is momentarily made to input D, that point goes to "0", and $\bar{Q}$ goes to "1". This, being fed back, means that both inputs A and C are at "1" and Q goes to "0". Since input B is now "0", $\bar{Q}$ remains at "1" and further input signals at D are inneffective. The situation is maintained, with Q low and $\bar{Q}$ high, until the switch is operated making input C go to "0". The bistable then changes its state, Q going to logic "1" and $\bar{Q}$ to logic "0".

Note that in the absence of the external resistors, if both inputs C and D are at logic "0" both outputs go to logic "1" and remain in that state. However, if C and D are both at logic "1", both Q and $\bar{Q}$ attempt to go to "0" and, due to the feedback arrangement the output state is indeterminate. It is this fact which restricts the use of the RS latch.

Bistable latch

A schematic diagram of one element of an SN 7475 quadruple bistable latch, shown in Fig. 9.23a, comprises four AND gates, two NOR gates and one inverter. For a NOR gate the output is at "0" if one or more of its inputs are at "1". Thus, if Q is at "1", the

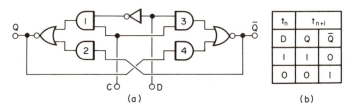

Fig. 9.23. Schematic diagram of one element of an SN 7475 quadruple bistable latch.

feedback via gate 4 ensures that $\bar{Q}$ is at "0". Let this be a starting condition and let the data input D be at "0". The action of the device may be studied by allowing the clock input C to move from "0" to "1" and back to "0", i.e. by simulating a clock pulse.

As C moves from "0" to "1", the two inputs to gate 1 become "1", its output goes to "1", Q switches to "0" and the output of gate 4 goes to "0". Also, with D at "0" the output of gate 3 is at "0", so $\bar{Q}$ switches to "1". When the clock returns to "0", the logic "1" at $\bar{Q}$

fed back via gate 2 ensures that Q remains at "0", so the effect of the clock pulse is to transfer the data input level to the Q output. The action is summed up in the truth table of Fig. 9.23b, in which t_n represents the state before the application of the clock pulse and t_{n+1} the state after the clock pulse. Note that the presence of the inverter ensures that the inputs to the two sides of the bistable are different, and the indeterminate state of the RS latch cannot arise in the bistable latch.

Type D flip-flop

The action of this edge-triggered device is explained with reference to the simplified logic diagram of an SN 7474 shown in Fig. 9.24. It is made up of three coupled RS latches. For a data input "D" and with the clock initially at "0", the outputs of gates 1, 2, 3

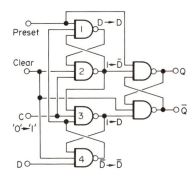

Fig. 9.24. Simplified logic diagram of an SN 7474 type D flip-flop.

and 4 are "D", "1", "1" and "$\bar{D}$", respectively, where $\bar{D}=$ "0" if $D=$ "1" and vice versa. As the clock level changes to "1", 1 and 4 outputs remain unchanged, 2 goes to "$\bar{D}$" and 3 goes to "D", as is indicated in the diagram. As a result, the data level "D" is transferred to output Q and "$\bar{D}$" appears at $\bar{Q}$.

When used in counters and shift registers (see Fig. 9.25), the data level D is constantly changing between logic "1" and logic "0" and it is possible in these applications for edge-triggered devices to mis-trigger. Figure 9.26 represents the leading edge of a typical clock pulse and three different regions have been indicated. In the *transition region*, between 0.8 V and 2.0 V, gates are operating in a

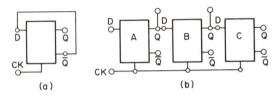

Fig. 9.25. The type D flip-flop used as (a) a binary counter and (b) a shift register.

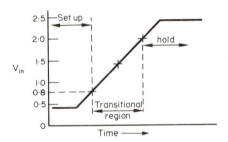

Fig. 9.26. Leading edge of a typical clock pulse. Transition is assumed to occur when $V_{in} = 1.4$ V.

linear mode, and it is within this region that data is transferred from input to output. The actual voltage at which transfer occurs depends upon the propagation delay time of the individual gates, being typically 1.4 V. If in this region the data level changes, then the switched output level will be indeterminate. To avoid this form of mistriggering and, taking account of the spread of propagation delay times of individual gates, it is recommended that with these devices, clock pulse rise times should not exceed 25 ns.

Master–slave JK flip-flops

In the shift register illustrated in Fig. 9.25b all three bistables are clocked simultaneously. Thus if the input to stage A is "1" and the Q outputs of A, B and C are initially "0", "1" and "0", respectively, then after one clock pulse these ideally become "1", "0" and "1". The binary number so represented has moved along the register one place. However, as has already been discussed, the actual input voltage level at which the output of a given device changes state can be different from another similar device, so it cannot be assumed that all bistables of the register operate simultaneously. Thus, if bistable A changes state before bistable B, then instead of accepting a logic "0" input, bistable B will accept a logic "1" input. As a result, after one clock pulse the three Q outputs will give the erroneous number "111" instead of "101". To prevent such an error some means must be found of storing the correct input data to each bistable over the critical period during which triggering occurs. This is done in devices using the master–slave principle, typified by the dual flip-flop SN 7476, one stage of which is illustrated in the functional diagram of Fig. 9.27. Two cross-coupled NOR gates form a *master* latching circuit, and two NAND gates form a *slave* output latching circuit.

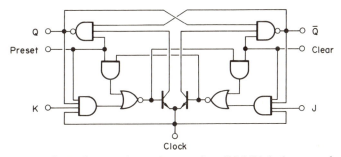

Fig. 9.27. Functional diagram of one element of an SN 7476 dual master–slave JK flip-flop.

Being one of the input signals to the J and K AND gates, the clock pulse controls the inputs to the master section. The state of the transistors which couple the master to the slave sections is determined by their base voltages, obtained from the NOR gates, combined with their emitter voltage which is obtained from the clock source. The clock pulse therefore also regulates the state of these two transistors, and hence the coupling between the two sections.

Referring to the clock pulse of Fig. 9.28a, at level 1 the slave is isolated from the master. Depending upon the signal levels of Q, $\bar{Q}$, J and K, at level 2 one of the input AND gates is "opened" and data is entered from the J and K inputs to the master section. At level 3 the J and K inputs are disabled, and data is transferred from the master to the slave output section at level 4. The truth table for this type of bistable is given in Fig. 9.28b. Note that any change in data which occurs before the J and K inputs are disabled can give rise to an

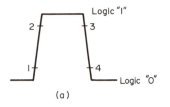

t_n		t_{n+1}
J	K	Q
O	O	Q_n
O	I	O
I	O	I
I	I	$\bar{Q}_n$

(a)

(b)

Fig. 9.28. (a) clock pulse to illustrate the switching sequence of an SN 7476 and (b) the relevant truth table.

erroneous output signal. It is therefore important that the correct data levels be maintained over the period for which the clock pulse is at logic "1".

In the SN 7476, provision is made for *preset* and *clear* facilities. The action of taking the preset input momentarily to logic "0" sets output Q to logic "1". Similarly, a negative going pulse at the clear input sets the Q output to logic "0". For normal operation in a shift register the preset and clear inputs are therefore held at logic "1", and the best means of doing this are discussed in Chapter 11.

9.11. Monostable multivibrators

Resistors and capacitors are the most common timing elements, although inductance-resistance timing is sometimes employed. The MMV is used principally for pulse forming and delay generation.

Collector-to-base coupled MMV

Referring to Fig. 9.29, the connection from the collector of T_1 to the diode, via R, biases the diode such that it is "open" when T_1 is conducting, and closed when T_2 is conducting (i.e. when T_1 is cut-off). Thus, a positive going waveform will be accepted to switch off T_1. When triggered, the positive excursion of the T_2 collector is transferred to the base of T_1 which is held beyond cut-off while C_B discharges through R_{B1}. When the base voltage of T_1 is sufficiently reduced, T_1 again conducts and T_2 is cut-off until the arrival of the next trigger pulse. Timing is thus effected by the time constant $C_B R_{B1}$ and is largely independent of the supply voltages.

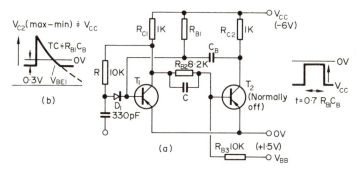

Fig. 9.29. Collector-to-base coupled MMV. A positive trigger at the input causes the generation of a rectangular pulse at the T_2 collector.

Design considerations

With the initial conditions of T_1 conducting and T_2 cut off, the collector voltage of $T_2 = V_{CC}$ and the collector voltage of T_1 is approximately zero. If the value of V_{BE1} for saturation is V'_{BE1} ($\doteqdot 0.3$ V), the voltage on the capacitor, $C_B \doteqdot V_{CC} - V'_{BE1}$. When the circuit is triggered, T_2 conducts and its collector voltage switches to the bottoming voltage, $V_{(\min 2)}$, i.e. a voltage excursion of $V_{CC} - V_{(\min 2)}$, and T_1 cuts off. The voltage on C_B is therefore increased to:

$$V_{\max} = (V_{CC} - V'_{BE}) + (V_{CC} - V_{(\min 2)})$$
$$= 2V_{CC} - V'_{BE} - V_{(\min 2)}. \qquad (9.4)$$

C_B now discharges through R_{B1} according to the law:

$$v = V_{\max} \exp(-t/\tau), \qquad (9.5)$$

where τ is the time constant $C_B R_{B1}$. This is plotted in Fig. 9.29b. T_1 will start to conduct again when

$$v = V_{CC} - V''_{BE1}, \qquad (9.6)$$

where V''_{BE1} is a little less negative than V'_{BE} ($\doteqdot -0.25$ V). Combining these three equations,

$$V_{CC} - V''_{BE1} = (2V_{CC} - V_{(\min)2} - V'_{BE}) \exp(-t/\tau). \qquad (9.7)$$

Neglecting $V_{(\min)2}$, V'_{BE} and V''_{BE1},

$$\exp(-t/\tau) \doteqdot 0.5.$$

Therefore

$$-t/\tau = \log_e 2,$$

and

$$t = 0.7 C_B R_{B1}. \tag{9.8}$$

If R_{B1} is returned to V'_{BB} instead of to V_{CC}, by similar considerations it may be shown that:

$$t/\tau = \log_e \frac{V_{CC} + V'_{BB}}{V_{CC}}. \tag{9.9}$$

Thus, the pulse length can be changed electrically by varying V'_{BB}.

The choice of collector resistor R_C is a compromise. For economy of collector current and low collector dissipation a relatively large value is used. On the other hand, a small value of R_C is required, giving a small collector time constant, for high-speed operation. The use of a small R_C has the added advantages, that it makes the circuit insensitive to external loading and also causes only a small voltage drop due to leakage current.

The positive base bias provided by R_{B3} and V_{BB} is only strictly necessary when operation over a wide temperature range is required.

Design steps
1. Select values for R_C and V_{CC} which will permit the necessary rise and fall times of the output pulse.
2. Calculate the saturation current, i.e. the current which will cause V_{CC} volts to be dropped across R_C.
3. Assume the minimum h_{FE} for the selected transistor and determine the base current required for bottoming; choose values of R_{B2} and R_{B3} to provide this current.
4. Using eqn. (9.8), calculate the values of C_B and R_{B1} to provide the required pulse length.

DESIGN EXAMPLE 9.2
Required a monostable multivibrator to provide an output pulse of 5 μs duration.

For this pulse length, rise and fall times of the order of 1 μs are necessary, and typical values for R_C and V_{CC} are 1 kΩ and -6 V.

Base resistors. $I_{sat} = V_{CC}/R_C = 6$ mA. With a minimum h_{FE} of 20, $I_B = I_{sat}/h_{FE} = 300 \ \mu$A.

(a) If positive bias is not used

$$R'_{B2} = 6 \text{ V}/0.3 \text{ mA} = 20 \text{ k}\Omega.$$

This represents a maximum value. Make $R'_{B2} = 15$ kΩ to allow for voltage variations.

(b) If positive bias is used and $V_{BB} = 1.5$ V, as shown in Fig. 9.30,

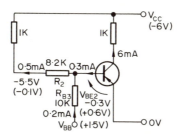

Fig. 9.30. Determination of the values of R_{B2} and R_{B3}.

let $R_{B3} = 10$ kΩ. Then, when T_2 is conducting the current in R_{B3},

$$I_3 = \frac{1.5 \text{ V} + 0.3 \text{ V}}{10 \text{ k}\Omega} \doteqdot 0.2 \text{ mA}.$$

The current in R_{B2},

$$I_2 = I_B + I_3 = 0.5 \text{ mA}.$$

Voltage across R_{B2},

$$V_1 = -V_{CC} - I_2 R_C + V_{BE},$$
$$= 6 - 0.5 - 0.3 \doteqdot 5 \text{ V}.$$

Thus,

$$R_{B2} = \frac{V_1}{I_2} = \frac{5 \text{ V}}{0.5 \text{ mA}} = 10 \text{ k}\Omega.$$

Again to allow for voltage variations, let R_{B2} have the preferred value of 8.2 kΩ. When T_1 is conducting its collector voltage $V'_{C1} = -0.1$ V. Thus,

$$V_{BE2} = V_{BB} - \frac{R_{B3}}{R_{B2} + R_{B3}}(V_{BB} - V'_{C1}),$$

$$= 1.5 \text{ V} - 0.9 \text{ V} = +0.6 \text{ V}.$$

The base emitter junction of T_2 is suitably reverse biased.

Timing network. In small transistors the maximum base current is of the order of 1 mA.

Thus, the minimum value of $R_{B1} = V_{CC}/I_{B(max)} = 6 \text{ V}/1 \text{ mA}$. Let R_{B1} be the preferred value of 5.6 lΩ.

From eqn. (9.8),

$$C_B = \frac{t}{0.7\,R_{B1}} \doteqdot \frac{5 \times 10^{-6}}{4 \times 10^3} = 1250 \text{ pF}.$$

9.12.   The direct coupled MMV (Fig. 9.31)

Operation

In the stable state, T_2, bottomed by the current in R_B, is conducting. A negative trigger pulse on the base of T_3 causes a reduction of the negative collector voltage of T_3 and T_1. This change is transferred to the base of T_2 via C_B, which is charged to $V_{CC} - V'_{BE}$.

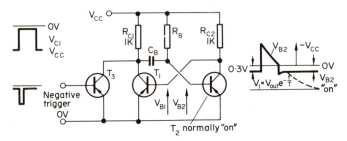

Fig. 9.31. The direct coupled MMV.

T_2 is thus cut off and held off for a period determined by the time constant $R_B C_B$. The exponential discharge of C_B is terminated, and T_2 switches on when $V_{B2} \doteqdot -0.25$ V. As in the previous example it can be shown that

$$t = \tau \log_e \frac{2V_{CC} - V'_{BE}}{V_{CC} - V''_{BE}}, \qquad (9.10)$$

and for $V_{CC} \gg V'_{BE}$,

$$t = 0.7C_B R_B. \qquad (9.11)$$

Example

Using an MA 240 transistor with $R_B = 10\,\text{k}\Omega$ and $C_B = 1000\,\text{pF}$, $\tau = 10^{-5}\,\text{s}$.

The waveforms obtained from such an arrangement are given in Fig. 9.32. Substituting values in eqn. (9.10) yields:

$$t = 10^{-5} \times 0.78 \doteq 8\,\mu\text{s}.$$

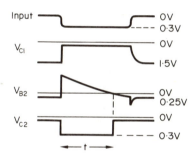

Fig. 9.32. Waveforms obtained from the circuit of Fig. 9.31.

Collector saturation voltage. The specification for the MA 240 requires that, for $I_C = 2\,\text{mA}$ and $I_B = 0.3\,\text{mA}$, the saturation collector voltage should not exceed 70 mV. It is typically 40 mV.

Base bias resistor. This should be small enough to allow T_2 to bottom.

If $R_{C2} = 1\,\text{k}\Omega$ and $V_{CC} = -1.5\,\text{V}$, $I_{C(\text{sat})} = 1.5\,\text{mA}$.

For a minimum $h_{FE} = 15$, $I_{B(\text{sat})} = 1.5\,\text{mA}/15 = 0.1\,\text{mA}$.

Making $R_B = 10\,\text{k}\Omega$ gives $I_B = 0.12\,\text{mA}$. If $I_{C(\text{sat})}$ is increased (by making $R_{C2} = 500\,\Omega$, for instance), 10 kΩ will be too high a value for R_B, and the circuit will have no stable state, but will oscillate. Thus, as with all transistor monostable multivibrators, to provide large variations in pulse width C_B must be varied and not R_B.

9.13.   Asymmetrical MMV

The circuit of Fig. 9.33 represents an asymmetrical monostable multivibrator. In its normal state T_1 is "on", and $V_{E1} \fallingdotseq +0.3$ V. The current $I_1 \fallingdotseq V_{EE}/R_{E1}$ is sufficient to ensure that V_{C1} holds T_2 "off".

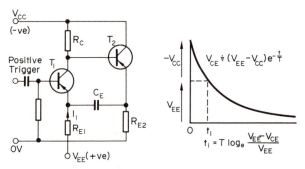

Fig. 9.33. Asymmetrical MMV. Because of the emitter coupling, T_2 has a "free" collector.

The application of a positive trigger causes a reduction in I_1, and the resulting change in V_{C1} allows T_2 to start conducting. The T_2 emitter therefore goes negative and, since C_E cannot charge instantaneously, the emitter of T_1 is also taken negative. T_1 regeneratively switches off, and T_2 bottoms. In this fully switched state, the emitters of both transistors are at approximately V_{CC} volts, and the voltage across R_{E1} is $V_{EE} - V_{CC}$ (where V_{CC} is negative for *pnp* transistors).

C_E now starts to charge through R_{E1} and when the charge reaches V_{CC} volts, T_1 starts to conduct. T_1 then switches on regeneratively and T_2 switches off again.

9.14.   Integrated circuit MMV

In integrated circuit form the monostable normally requires the use of external R–C timing components as, for instance, with the SN 74121. The dual-in-line package of this device is illustrated in Fig. 9.34a and three inputs are indicated. Providing that input B is held at logic "1", if either A_1 or A_2 are provided with a pulse, triggering occurs on the negative going edge of that pulse. If input B is set to logic "0", the operation of the monostable is inhibited.

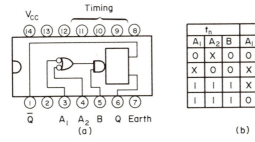

t_n			t_{n+1}		
A_1	A_2	B	A_1	A_2	B
0	X	0	0	X	1
X	0	0	X	0	1
1	1	1	X	0	1
1	1	1	0	X	1

(a)   (b)

Fig. 9.34. (a) Dual-in-line package of an SN 74121N MMV and (b) a truth table indicating the input conditions for which a pulse is initiated. The X indicates a "don't care" condition which may be either logic "1" or logic "0".

Alternatively, as indicated in the table of Fig. 9.34b, if both A_1 and A_2 are held at logic "0", triggering occurs when input B is taken to logic "1". Thus, an output pulse of predetermined width may be obtained from the trailing edge of a trigger pulse applied at the A inputs, or from the leading edge of a pulse applied at the B input. The device will respond to slow edges at the B input and may be used in this form of operation for level detecting purposes.

Timing

An internal timing resistor of approximately 2 kΩ is included in the integrated circuit and, if no extra resistance is required, pins 9 and 14 are connected together. If, however, a variable output pulse width is required, a variable resistor should be connected between these two pins. A maximum value of 40 kΩ is recommended for this purpose. With no external capacitance a pulse width of about 30 ns can be obtained, and for greater pulse widths a capacitor must be connected between pins 10 and 11. By suitable choice of external R–C components the SN 74121 can provide pulses of duration in the range 40 ns to 40 sec.

A hybrid circuit

Pulse widths of many seconds may also be obtained from the circuit of Fig. 9.35, which operates from the trailing edge of an input pulse. As the input goes to logic "0" the gate 1 output goes to "1". The output of gate 2, tied to V_{CC} by R_1, goes to logic "0" and thus falls by nearly 5 V. This causes T_1 to cut off, its collector rises to 5 V and

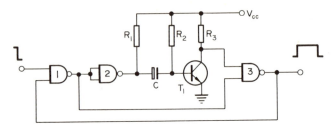

Fig. 9.35. A hybrid MMV. A pulse of several seconds duration can be generated, initiated by a "falling" edge at the input.

the output of gate 3 goes to "0". The capacitor now charges towards V_{CC} on a time constant CR_2, until the transistor again starts to conduct. The collector voltage now falls, gate 3 output goes to logic "1" and this, being fed back, causes gate 1 to go to "0" and gate 2 to "1", driving T_1 into full conduction.

The duration of the output pulse provided by this circuit is approximately $0.8CR_2$, the maximum value for R_2 being dependent upon the current gain of the transistor. Providing that input pulses of at least 1 μs duration are available, a suitable transistor is a 2N 3711 which permits R_2 to have values up to 330 kΩ.

9.15.   Astable multivibrators

The AMV is a free-running multivibrator which produces rectangular pulses at a predetermined repetition frequency. It may therefore be used as the basic timing circuit for sweep generators, counters, etc.

Figure 9.36 represents a symmetrical collector-to-base coupled

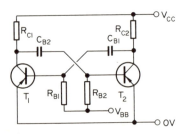

Fig. 9.36. Symmetrical AMV.

circuit, having an operation as follows. Assume an initial condition of T_1 conducting and T_2 cut-off. C_{B2} now charges through R_{B2} carrying the base of T_2 negative until T_2 starts to conduct. The collector voltage of T_2 then begins to rise, carrying the T_1 base positive; T_1 regeneratively cuts off and T_2 bottoms. C_{B1} now charges, the base of T_1 goes negative until T_1 conducts again, and the cycle repeats.

Design Considerations

The way base voltage varies with time is indicated in Fig. 9.37,

$$v_B = (-V_{CC} + V'_{BE} - V_{BB}) \exp(-t/\tau) + V_{BB},$$

where conduction takes place when v_B falls to approximately -0.3 V.

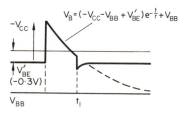

Fig. 9.37. Base waveform of the astable multivibrator.

If V'_{BE} is small compared with V_{CC} and V_{BB}, and this is usually the case, then:

$$V_{BB} = -(V_{CC} + V_{BB}) \exp(-t/\tau)$$

or,

$$t = \tau \log_e \left(1 + \frac{V_{CC}}{V_{BB}}\right)$$

$$= C_B R_B \log_e 2 \quad (\text{if } V_{CC} = V_{BB}).$$

Therefore,

$$t = 0.7 \, C_B R_B. \tag{9.12}$$

The period for a symmetrical system is $2t_1 = 1.4 \, C_B R_B$.

Design steps

1. Select suitable collector resistors and calculate the saturation current which will flow.

2. Using the minimum value of h_{FE} for the type of transistor to be used, determine the minimum base current which will cause this saturation current.

3. Calculate the maximum value of R_B to provide the necessary base current.

4. Using eqn. (9.12), evaluate C_B.

DESIGN EXAMPLE 9.3

Required, an astable multivibrator having a period of 0.1 ms (i.e. a p.r.f. of 10 kHz), using a -1.5 V supply voltage. Let the transistor chosen be an MA 240 with a quoted minimum h_{FE} of 15. Make the collector resistors 2.2 kΩ.

Collector saturation current

$$I_{C(\text{sat})} = \frac{V_{CC}}{R_C} = \frac{1.5 \text{ V}}{2.2 \text{ k}\Omega} = 0.68 \text{ mA}.$$

Minimum base current

$$I_{B(\text{min})} = \frac{I_{C(\text{sat})}}{h_{FE(\text{min})}} = \frac{0.68 \text{ mA}}{15} = 45 \text{ } \mu\text{A}.$$

The transistor will conduct when $V''_{BE} = -0.3$ V. Thus,

$$R_{B(\text{max})} = \frac{V_{CC} - V''_{BE}}{I_{B(\text{min})}} = \frac{1.5 - 0.3 \text{ V}}{45 \text{ } \mu\text{A}} = 27 \text{ k}\Omega.$$

This is the maximum value. Let the design value be 22 kΩ, to ensure saturation.

Half period $= 0.7C_BR_B = 50 \text{ } \mu\text{s}.$

Therefore

$$C_B = \frac{5 \times 10^{-5}}{0.7 \times 22 \times 10^3} = 3300 \text{ pF}.$$

The completed circuit is given in Fig. 9.38.

The collector waveform, obtained from this circuit, can be made more rectangular by the use of smaller collector resistors, thus reducing the time constant $R_C C_B$. Alternatively use may be made of the Darlington connection shown in Fig. 9.39. This connection gives a current gain of $(h_{FE})^2$, which, when substituted in the above calculations, leads to a bigger R_B and smaller C_B. The $R_C C_B$ time constant is thus reduced.

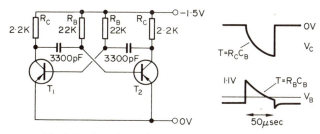

Fig. 9.38. Completed circuit of Design Example 9.3.

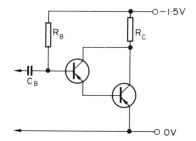

Fig. 9.39. The use of the Darlington connection leads to a better collector waveform than that obtained from the network of Fig. 9.38.

9.16 Emitter-coupled AMV

The circuit has the form of Fig. 9.40 and is similar to the previously described emitter coupled MMV. The output waveform can be obtained from a "free" collector, i.e. one which does not enter directly into the feedback loop.

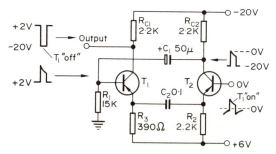

Fig. 9.40. Emitter-coupled AMV. The free collector of this network provides a well-defined rectangular pulse.

Operation

When T_2 starts conducting, the base of T_1 is taken positive by the full excursion of the T_2 collector voltage, i.e. 20 V. Since the base of T_1 was originally held at 2 V positive by the base current in R_1, V_{B1} becomes +22 V and the emitter voltage is 2 V.

The emitter of T_2 is held at approximately 0 V, because the base is earthed, and the T_1 emitter voltage rises on a time constant of approximately C_2R_3 as C_2 charges to +6 V. The charging current, which is drawn from the emitter of T_2, falls off exponentially and consequently the collector current of T_2 is reduced, causing the collector to become more negative.

This charge is transferred to the base of T_1 via C_1 (which has no effect on the timing). Thus the T_1 base and emitter voltages approach equality and when the base becomes sufficiently negative with respect to the emitter, T_1 conducts. The resulting voltage produced across R_3 is transferred to the emitter of T_2 making $V_{E2} \doteq -3.5$ V, and T_2 is cut off.

The collector voltage of T_2 therefore changes to V_{CC} and this change is applied to the base of T_1, completing the regenerative loop. The emitter voltage of T_2 now rises from -3.5 V towards $+6$ V on the time constant C_2R_2. When the emitter reaches a slight positive voltage, T_2 conducts and the cycle repeats.

9.17.   Complementary AMV

The negative resistance arrangement of § 9.9 may be used with an R–C network as an astable multivibrator, as shown in Fig. 9.41.

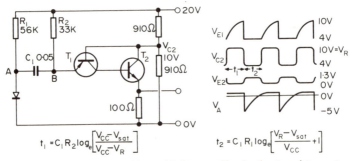

Fig. 9.41. Complementary astable multivibrator. V_{sat} is the transistor saturation voltage.

Operation

With both transistors "off" V_{C2} is at 10 V, and point A is held at 0 V by the diode. Point B now rises towards 20 V on the time constant C_1R_2 until it is sufficiently positive, with respect to V_{C2}, to cause T_1 to conduct. This in turn brings T_2 into conduction. The current drawn by T_2 collector causes V_{C2} to fall, and this fall is transferred to point A via T_1 and C_1. Point A is thus taken negative. It now rises towards 20 V on the time constant C_1R_1, but is caught at 0 V by the "catching" diode, and the transistors are switched off.

9.18.   Integrated circuit AMV

An astable multivibrator may be made using three NAND gates, as shown in Fig. 9.42. This illustrates the use of an SN 7400 quadruple 2-input device, the fourth gate acting as a buffer output stage.

Initially, let the inputs to gate 1 be taken to logic "0". Its output switches to "1" and C starts to charge exponentially on a time constant CR. When it reaches the transition voltage, gate 2 output switches to logic "0", and after a similar delay gate 3 output switches to "1". Being fed back, this causes gate 1 to change its state and the process continues with each gate in the closed-loop switching in succession.

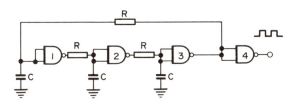

Fig. 9.42. A three-NAND-gate AMV. Gate 4 acts as a buffer stage.

Period of oscillation

The data sheet for a NAND gate in the 74 series gives the following worst-case conditions for guaranteed operation:

Maximum logic "0" input, for a logic "1" output = 0.8 V.
Minimum logic "1" input, for a logic "0" output = 2.0 V.
Maximum logic "0" output = 0.4 V.
Minimum logic "1" output = 2.4 V.

It follows that transition takes place when an input is in the range 0.8 to 2.0 V. Assume that it occurs for an input at 1.4 V and, additionally, assume that the output switches between 0.2 and 3.6 V.

At time t the charge on the capacitor is:

$$v(t) = V_{oo}[1 - \exp(-t/CR)],$$

where V_{oo} is the aiming voltage.

To find the time for the charge to reach the transition voltage,

$$(1.4 - 0.2) = (3.6 - 0.2)[1 - \exp(-t/CR)],$$

$$1.2 - 3.4 = -3.4 \exp(-t/CR),$$

therefore, $\exp(-t/CR) = 0.65$, from which $t = 0.43\ CR$. The period of one complete oscillation, which is made up of six such delays, is thus $2.5\ CR$.

Note that as a gate output switches to "1", it must provide the charging current for the capacitor and the necessary input current for the following gate. This sets a limit to the maximum value of resistance which may be used for guaranteed operation, being typically 500 Ω.

Example. If 470 Ω resistors are used, for a 1-MHz oscillator, $10^{-6} = 2.5 \times C \times 470$, from which $C = 850$ pF.

9.19. Voltage-controlled AMV

A voltage-controlled oscillator may be made using two NAND gates as shown in Fig. 9.43. Using the worst case conditions, as before, it is again assumed that the gate outputs switch between 0.2

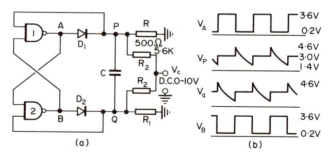

(a)   (b)

Fig. 9.43. (a) Voltage-controlled AMV with (b) the relevant waveforms.

and 3.6 V. With the corresponding diodes cut-off the quiescent voltages at P and Q are

$$v_o = V_c \frac{R_1}{R_1 + R_2},$$

where V_c is the frequency control voltage. The resistors must be chosen such that for maximum V_c, v_o does not exceed 0.8 V, so that at all times it represents logic "0".

Operation

If silicon diodes are used, then 0.6 V will be dropped across them when conducting. As a starting-point, let gate 1 be at logic "1", so that D_1 conducts and $V_p = 3.6 - 0.6 = 3$ V. At the same time, gate 2 will be at logic "0", D_2 will be "closed" and V_q will be falling towards v_o. When it reaches the transition voltage 1.4 V switch-over occurs, gate 2 going to "1" and gate 1 to "0". D_2 now conducts, V_q rises sharply to 3 V, and this rise of $3 - 1.4 = 1.6$ V is transferred to point P. V_p thus rises to 4.6 V and then decays exponentially on a time constant CR_1 towards v_o. When it reaches 1.4 V switch-over occurs in the opposite direction. The process continues with points P and Q alternately rising rapidly to 4.6 V and then decaying to 1.4 V, as shown in the waveforms of Fig. 9.43b.

Period of oscillation

The exponential decay is from 4.6 V to 1.4 V with v_o as the aiming voltage.

$$v(t) = V \exp(-t/\tau).$$

Thus,

$$(1.4 - v_o) = (4.6 - v_o) \exp(-t/CR).$$

For $v_o = 0$, $\exp(-t/CR) = 0.3$, so $t_1 = 1.2 \, CR$.
For $v_o = 0.8$, $\exp(-t/CR) = 0.158$, so $t_2 = 1.85 \, CR$.
The period of one complete oscillation is $2t$, the frequency is $\frac{1}{2}t$, and the ratio of maximum to minimum frequencies is $t_2/t_1 = 1.54$.

By comparison, the Motorola MC 4024 provides a variation of output frequency over a 3.5 to 1 range as an input-control voltage is varied between 1 and 5 V. This typical device includes two voltage-controlled multivibrators in one package, each using a totem-pole output stage to provide an output compatible with TTL logic levels. The actual operating frequency range is determined by the addition of an external capacitor, and the maximum operating frequency is typically 30 MHz.

9.20.   Pulse generators

It is frequently required that the rectangular waveform obtained from an AMV be used to provide a narrow pulse at either its leading or trailing edge, or both. This may be accomplished by the simple "differentiating" network of Fig. 9.44a. Since C_d cannot charge instantaneously, the leading edge of the input waveform appears across R_d. The capacitor C_d now charges on the time constant $C_d R_d$,

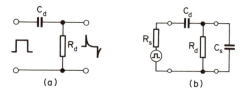

Fig. 9.44. Simple "differentiating" network.

and the voltage across R_d falls exponentially on the same time constant. After a time $4C_d R_d$, the voltage across the resistor is approximately zero and remains thus until the arrival of the trailing edge. The sequence is then repeated in the opposite direction. The output from such a network, in response to an input rectangular waveform of duration D, is given in Fig. 9.45, and shows the effect of varying the time constant $C_d R_d$.

In practice, the driving circuit will have some resistance R_s and the resistor R_d will probably be shunted by a capacitance C_s, e.g. the input capacitance of an amplifier to which the network is connected. The effective circuit is therefore that of Fig. 9.44b. The leading edge of the output waveform now rises on the time constant $C_s R_s$, but as this may be made very small, rise times of the order of a fraction of a microsecond are possible, provided that the rise time of the input waveform leading edge is faster than this. The presence of C_s also causes a reduction in the amplitude of the output signal. Thus,

$$\frac{V_{\text{out}}}{V_{\text{in}}} = \frac{C_d}{C_s + C_d}. \qquad (9.13)$$

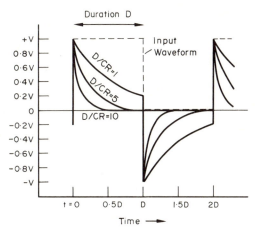

Fig. 9.45. Response of simple "differentiating" network to a rectangular waveform.

The output from a simple differentiating circuit is seen to be a positive "spike", synchronous with the positive-going leading edge of a rectangular input waveform, and a negative "spike" synchronous with the negative going trailing edge. These spikes may be squared-off and unwanted spikes removed by the use of limiter circuits.

Even when limited, the pulse is not rectangular. However, it can be made to approach the rectangular shape by the use of a small value of inductance in series with R_d. If L is made equal to $\frac{1}{2}C_sR_d^2$, then the resulting resonant effect will produce a pulse which is broader at the top and which has a steeper trailing edge. An alternative method of producing a narrow pulse from the trailing edge of a square waveform is given in Fig. 9.46.

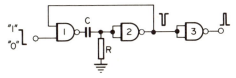

Fig. 9.46. The "differentiating" network used with NAND gates to provide a narrow rectangular pulse.

As the output of gate 1 goes to logic "1", say to 3.6 V, this rise is transmitted through the capacitor and appears across R. Gate 2 therefore switches to logic "0". The voltage across R now decays exponentially, as before, and as it passes through logic "0", gate 2 output returns to logic "1". As the logic "0" input current to gate 2 must pass through R, the resistance value is restricted to about 500 Ω.

9.21. Linear sweep generators

If the output from a C–R combination is taken from across the capacitor, as in Fig. 9.47a the network acts as an "integrator". In fact the true integration of a rectangular waveform is a triangular waveform, i.e. one in which the voltage rises and falls linearly with time. In the simple network shown, however, both rise and fall are exponential, with a time constant C_iR_i.

Figure 9.47b represents an ideal linear sweep waveform having the law, $V = at$, for t greater than 0. Such a waveform is required for time-bases and is also used for comparator circuits.

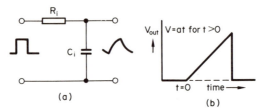

(a)   (b)

Fig. 9.47. (a) Simple "integrating" network. (b) Ideal linear sweep waveform.

A simple way of providing a sweep voltage is to charge a capacitor through a large resistor. The charge is exponential, of course, as is shown in Fig. 9.48, but if only the first part of the output waveform is used, then a reasonably linear rise is obtained. For instance, if v_c is

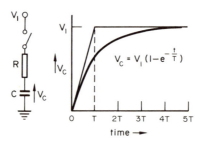

Fig. 9.48. Exponential rise in V_c as a capacitor is charged through a resistor.

allowed to rise to only 10 per cent of the full voltage, the non-linearity is 5 per cent:

$$v_c = V_1[1 - \exp(-t/\tau)],$$

$$v_c = \frac{V_1 t}{\tau}\left[1 - \frac{t}{2\tau} + \frac{t^2}{6\tau^2}\cdots\right],$$

$$= at\left[1 - \frac{t}{2\tau} + \frac{t^2}{6\tau^2}\cdots\right],$$

where $a = V_1/\tau$.

Thus, for small values of t, $v_c = at$ (as in Fig. 9.47b).

At the end of the required sweep, the capacitor must be discharged, and this may be done by a transistor connected as in Fig. 9.49. When non-conducting, i.e. during the sweep period, the transistor should be reverse biased. A silicon transistor is preferred to a germanium type in this application because of its low leakage current.

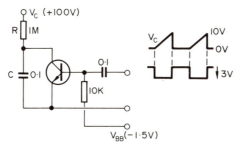

Fig. 9.49. Use of a transistor to discharge the capacitor of an RC sweep network.

9.22. Use of a constant-current generator (Fig. 9.50)

For a given supply voltage, performance can be improved by charging the capacitor from a constant current generator instead of through a resistor. For a rise time of 10 V in 10 ms,

$$\frac{dV}{dt} = \frac{I}{C} = 1000 \text{ V/s}.$$

Let I be 1 mA, then $C = 1 \mu\text{F}$.

$$I = \alpha I_E \doteqdot \frac{V_{B2}}{R_E}.$$

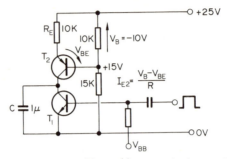

Fig. 9.50. Linear sweep generator, T_2 provides a constant current of approximately 1 mA.

Therefore

$$R_E = 10\,k\Omega.$$

If T_2 is a silicon transistor, the resistance of the current source will be approximately r_c, i.e. several megohms.

9.23.   Sawtooth generator using avalanche switching

If the characteristics of a transistor are plotted for collector voltages greater than those normally used, they take the form of Fig. 9.51. With increasing collector voltage a region is reached where large collector currents result from very small changes in V_C. This region is known as the *avalanche region* and occurs at a collector voltage at which h_{fb} tends to unity. The effect of reverse biasing the base of the transistor is to hold off the break-down point to a considerably greater

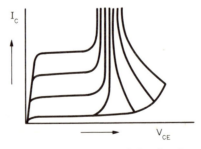

Fig. 9.51. Germanium alloy transistor characteristics showing avalanche breakdown region.

voltage. Once breakdown is initiated however, the voltage across the transistor falls to the lower value if the base resistor is sufficiently large. Figure 9.51 represents the breakdown characteristic of a germanium alloy transistor and in Fig. 9.52 is drawn the circuit diagram of a sawtooth generator making use of this breakdown phenomenon.

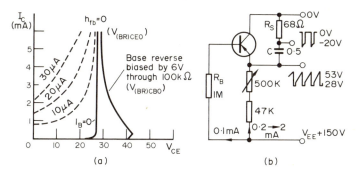

Fig. 9.52. Linear sawtooth generator using avalanche breakdown.

Sweep amplitude

The amplitude of the sweep obtained from such a circuit is effectively determined by the emitter voltage swing. The approximate range of this swing is between the breakdown voltages for (a) the collector–base junction with emitter open circuit, $V_{(BR)CB0}$, and (b) the collector–emitter with base open circuit, $V_{(BR)CE0}$. It is usually of the order of 20 V, and in this example is from 53 to 28 V.

Operation

At the start of the sweep the base of the transistor is held at $V_{(BR)CB0}$. The capacitor C charges through the emitter resistor until the emitter–base junction becomes forward biased (i.e. the emitter reaches $V_{(BR)CB0}$). The voltage across the transistor then falls to $V_{(BR)CE0}$.

This transition is extremely rapid because of the negative resistance effect exhibited when the transistor current increases as the voltage decreases.

Design considerations

Supply voltage. To obtain a linear sawtooth waveform the capacitor should be charged from a constant current source, and the use of a high voltage and large series resistor is therefore indicated. The supply voltage should be at least five times the sawtooth amplitude.

Thus, in Fig. 9.52, to provide a sawtooth amplitude of 20 V, let V_{EE} be 150 V. The mean emitter voltage is approximately 40 V, and the voltage across the emitter resistor V_R is 110 V.

Sweep speed dV/dt.   For a maximum sweep speed of 20 V in 5 ms,

$$\frac{dV}{dt} = \frac{20}{5 \times 10^{-3}} = 4 \times 10^3 \text{ V/s},$$

$Q = CV$, where Q is the charge on the capacitor,

$$i = \frac{dQ}{dt} = C\frac{dV}{dt},$$

where V is the voltage across C.

If $C = 0.5 \ \mu$F, $i = 0.5 \times 10^{-6} \times 4 \times 10^3 = 2$ mA.

This current is supplied through the emitter resistor. Thus,

$$i = V_R/R_E \quad \text{and} \quad R_E = \frac{110 \text{ V}}{2 \text{ mA}} = 55 \text{ k}\Omega.$$

Let R_E be a 47-kΩ resistor in series with a 500-kΩ variable resistor. This will enable the sweep duration to be varied over the range 5–50 ms.

Base resistor R_B.   This should be sufficiently large to limit the collector dissipation $P_C = I_B \cdot V_{(BR)CB0}$. The dissipation is limited to 5 mW if $R_B = 1$ MΩ, so this is a suitable value.

Peak emitter current.   A small value resistor R_S in series with the capacitor serves to limit the peak emitter current which might otherwise damage the transistor. In this example it is made 68 Ω and the peak emitter current is limited to about 0.3 mA. A large negative-going pulse is obtainable across R_S, synchronous with the start of the sweep waveform.

9.24. Miller timebase generator

Consider an amplifier with low input resistance, and having a transfer impedance $Z_t = v_{out}/i_{in}$, connected as in Fig. 9.53. The

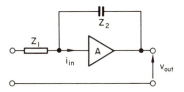

Fig. 9.53. Amplifier with transfer impedance Z_t connected as a Miller timebase generator.

forward voltage transfer function,

$$\frac{v_{out}(s)}{v_{in}(s)} = -\frac{Z_2}{Z_1}\frac{1}{1-Z_2/Z_t},$$

$$= -\frac{1}{sCR}\frac{1}{1-1/sCZ_t},$$

$$= \frac{1}{CR}\frac{1}{s-1/CZ_t},$$

$$\frac{v_{out}(t)}{v_{in}(t)} = \frac{Z_t}{R}[1-\exp{(t/CZ_t)}], \tag{9.14}$$

where Z_t is a negative quantity for negative feedback. Expanding eqn. (9.14) and for an input step of V_1 volts,

$$v_{out}(t) = -\frac{V_1 Z_t}{R}\left[\frac{t}{CZ_t}+\frac{1}{2}\left(\frac{t}{CZ_t}\right)^2+\frac{1}{6}\left(\frac{t}{CZ_t}\right)^3+\cdots\right]$$

$$= -\frac{V_1 t}{CR}\left[1+\frac{1}{2}\left(\frac{t}{CZ_t}\right)+\frac{1}{6}\left(\frac{t}{CZ_t}\right)^2+\cdots\right].$$

Thus, for an error less than 1 per cent at $t = CR$, $50R/Z_t < 1$.

Design considerations (Fig. 9.54)

During the sweep period the capacitor is charged through R and the recovery is on the time constant CR_C. Ideally, it is required to maintain a constant current out of the capacitor. Since V_{BE} does not

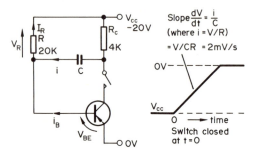

Fig. 9.54. Basic circuit of a transistor Miller timebase generator.

change by more than a fraction of a volt the voltage across R, and hence the current through it, is effectively constant. Thus,

$$I_R = V_{CC}/R. \qquad (9.15)$$

Not all this current is drawn from C, however, because of the base current which flows, but the circuit is designed so that i_B forms only a small part of I_R.

Output voltage

The output waveform varies between 0 V (transistor saturated) and V_{CC} volts (transistor cut-off). Thus, maximum current flows through R_C with the transistor saturated:

$$I_{max} = V_{CC}/R_C. \qquad (9.16)$$

Using the values of Fig. 9.54,

$$I_{max} = 20 \text{ V}/4 \text{ k}\Omega = 5 \text{ mA}.$$

While the time base is running C requires an additional 1 mA, so the saturation current to be supplied from the transistor is 6 mA.

Base current

The maximum base current

$$i_B = \frac{I_{C(sat)}}{h_{FE}} = \frac{6 \text{ mA}}{80} \doteq 75 \text{ } \mu\text{A}.$$

At the end of the sweep i_C is thus reduced by 75 μA, i.e. an error of 7.5 per cent.

Design steps
1. Using eqn. (9.16) select a value for R_C to provide several milliamps maximum current.
2. Calculate the base current required for saturation.
3. Make R of such value that the percentage of the current through it, provided by i_B, equals the acceptable percentage error by which the current may deviate.
4. Select C to give the required time constant and check that the recovery time constant CR_C is acceptable.
5. Arrange suitable switching circuitry.

DESIGN EXAMPLE 9.4

Required, a timebase waveform of 20 V amplitude, 10 ms duration, and 10 ms recovery. The waveform is to have a linearity tolerance of 5 per cent.

Since the sweep amplitude is to be 20 V this voltage is chosen for V_{CC}.

Collector resistor R_C. To ensure a current of several milliamps, so that the full current gain, h_{FE}, of the transistor is used and a low output resistance is obtained, let $R_C = 4 \text{ k}\Omega$.

Base current. For an h_{FE} of 80,

$$i_{B(\text{max})} = \frac{20 \text{ V}}{4 \text{ k}\Omega} \times \frac{1}{80} = 60 \ \mu\text{A}.$$

Resistor R. For 5 per cent error, I_R should be 20 times $i_{B(\text{max})}$ ($\doteqdot 1$ mA). Therefore,

$$R = V_{CC}/I_R = \frac{20 \text{ V}}{1 \text{ mA}} = 20 \text{ k}\Omega.$$

Capacitor.

$$\frac{dV}{dt} = \frac{20 \text{ V}}{10 \text{ ms}} = 2000 \text{ V/s} = \frac{V}{CR}.$$

$$C = \frac{V}{R} \frac{dt}{dV} = \frac{20 \text{ V}}{2 \times 10^3 \times 20 \times 10^3} = 0.5 \ \mu\text{F}.$$

Recovery time. The recovery time constant $CR_C = 0.5 \times 10^{-6} \times 4 \times 10^3 = 2$ ms. The capacitor will therefore be able to charge 20 V in 10 ms and the specification is met.

Gating.   In the final circuit of Fig. 9.55, T_2 is used as a switch. It acts as a common base stage and does not change the gain appreciably.

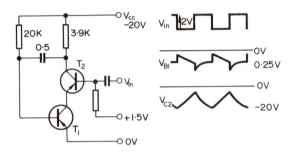

Fig. 9.55. Completed circuit of Design Example 9.4. Gating is effected by T_2.

9.25.   Reduction of recovery time

The recovery time which equals $5CR_C$, can be reduced by decreasing either R_C or C. Reduction of R_C requires an increase in base current which will reduce linearity. Alternatively, a reduction in C necessitates a larger value for R and again linearity is reduced. A solution is to make use of the Darlington connection which increases the current gain to approximately $(h_{FE})^2$. The base current is then reduced by $(h_{FE})^{-1}$ permitting R to be increased without a reduction in linearity. The circuit is drawn in Fig. 9.56.

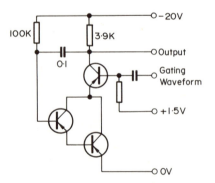

Fig. 9.56. Use of Darlington connection to reduce recovery time.

If $R = 100 \, k\Omega$ for a 10-ms sweep duration $C = 1 \, \mu F$, and the recovery time, $5CR_C = 2$ ms. This arrangement will provide a linearity at least 10 times better than in the previous example.

9.26. Integrated circuit waveform generator/VCO

Integrated circuits are available which simultaneously produce sine, square and triangular waveforms. Such a device is the type 8038 capable of providing frequencies, or PRFs, in the range 0.001 Hz to 1 MHz.

Figure 9.57a illustrates one arrangement of the external circuitry which is necessary with this waveform generator, and the phase relationships between the three outputs are shown in Fig. 9.57b. Adjustment of the potentiometer between pins 4 and 5 enable the duty cycle of the output waveforms to be varied. Thus, pulses may be obtained instead of the square waveform, and the triangular waveform can be replaced by a sawtooth.

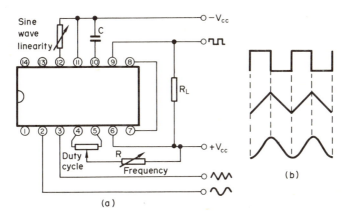

Fig. 9.57. Type 8038 waveform generator, illustrating (a) the various controls and (b) the phase relationship of the output waveforms.

The operating range of frequencies is determined by the value of the capacitor C, and the makers recommend that, for optimum performance, the charging current should be restricted within the range $10 \, \mu A$ to 1 mA, a current ratio of 100. This current is determined by V_{CC} and the value of the resistor R so, for a given V_{CC},

R may be varied in the same ratio. Since the frequency $f = 0.15/RC$, it follows that for a given capacitor, optimum performance is obtainable over a range of frequencies in the ratio of 100 to 1.

For use as a voltage-controlled oscillator the link between pins 7 and 8 is removed and the control voltage is applied between pin 8 and V_{CC}.

CHAPTER 10

Digital Techniques

INTRODUCTION

Whereas the analogue operations considered in previous chapters use variables with values lying in a linear range between an upper and lower limit, a digital variable has only two levels. These can be considered as the upper and lower boundaries of the analogue range (see Fig. 10.1). The two levels, or states, are frequently referred to as *high* and *low*, indicating the voltage condition. Alternatively they can be called *true* or *false*, terms which relate to Boolean logic

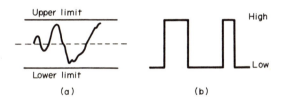

Fig. 10.1. An analogue signal (a) can take all values between the upper and lower limits. The ideal digital signal (b) has only two levels.

concepts, or simply *on* and *off* which express the states for switch and relay systems. A further form regards the digital signal as a set of ones (1) and zeros (0). This is consistent with the binary number representation which uses only two states.

Because of their efficiency, digital methods are widely used for the transmission, selection and storage of information, even though the input and output is in continuous or analogue form. For arithmetic operations, digital methods do not have the accuracy limitation of systems employing analogue devices.

403

10.1. Interface elements

In other than purely arithmetic systems there is a requirement for elements which link together the two types of systems. The basic interface elements are shown in Fig. 10.2.

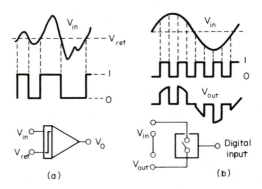

Fig. 10.2. (a) If the reference level is at zero, the comparator operates as a zero crossing detector. (b) The digital-analogue switch passes the analogue signal when the digital input is high.

They are:

- (a) *the comparator*, which converts an analogue signal above a given reference level to a "1", and below to "0", and
- (b) *the digitally controlled switch*. This passes an analogue signal only when the digital input is "1".

Practical forms

(a) *Comparator.* Figure 10.3a shows a simple form of comparator which uses an operational amplifier in open loop. The output voltage is restricted by the Zener diode to $+5\,V$ in the positive direction, and to $-0.5\,V$ in the negative direction. These output voltages are consistent with digital logic levels.

(b) *Logic-controlled analogue switch.* Figure 10.3b shows how a junction field effect transistor can be employed as an analogue switch. Transistors T_1 and T_2 convert the logic level input to a bipolar voltage. Thus when the input is high (i.e. a "1"), the collector of T_2 is positive and the gate of the FET "floating". The channel resistance under these conditions is in the region of 20 to 200 Ω. On

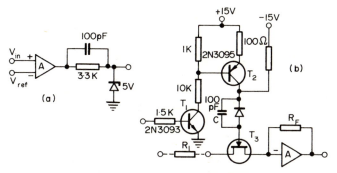

Fig. 10.3. (a) Simple comparator using an operational amplifier. The output is limited in the negative direction by the forward diode-conduction voltage, and in the positive direction by the 5-V zener breakdown. (b) A junction FET can be used as an analogue switch. T_1 and T_2 provide the required gate voltages.

removal of the digital input, the gate is taken negative and the channel becomes a high resistance. The capacitor C supplies charge to assist the switching.

To ensure that the gate–source voltage is adequate, the FET switch is usually placed at the virtual earth of a parallel–parallel connected feedback amplifier.

10.2. Basic combinational logic elements

(a) *OR gate.* This is a parallel-path concept. In Fig. 10.4a, if either or both switches are closed the lamp will light. Conversely, if neither switch is closed the lamp will be unlit. If the lamp is represented by the letter C and the switches by A and B, the logic OR expression is

$$A + B = C. \tag{10.1}$$

A simple diode network can perform this function. In Fig. 10.4a if either anode is raised by the appropriate voltage, the common cathode will follow. A truth table (so named because it is derived from the theory of logical propositions) gives all the possible combinations of the input variables. While only the two inputs A and B are shown, these can be extended to any number.

(b) *AND gate.* If the switches are in series, as in Fig. 10.4b, the lamp will be energized only when both switches are closed. Thus

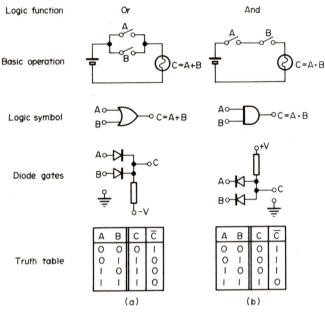

Fig. 10.4. Basic logic elements.

there is only one state which will provide an output. The logical statement is

$$A \cdot B = C \tag{10.2}$$

The AND function can be performed by diodes with the cathodes as input terminals. If any cathode is held low the common anode will remain low. Only when all the cathodes are high will the output be able to rise, since the diode with the lowest cathode voltage conducts and holds the anode at that voltage plus the forward diode voltage.

Venn diagram. The above relationships can be shown on the Venn diagram of Fig. 10.5, where the total shaded region represents $A + B$, and the double shaded region $A \cdot B$.

(c) *NOT operation.* An inverting amplifier performs the operation of negation. If the input to an amplifier is A, then the output is NOT A, written as $\bar{A}$. The unshaded area of the Venn diagram thus represents $\overline{A + B}$. The symbols for a negator, or inverter, are shown in Fig. 10.6a.

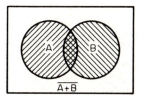

Fig. 10.5. Total shaded region represents $A + B$ (A OR B). The double-shaded region represents $A \cdot B$ (A AND B).

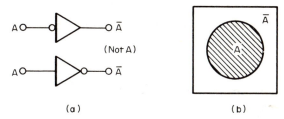

(a)   (b)

Fig. 10.6. (a) Symbol for an inverter. The circle placed either before or after the amplifier indicates inversion. (b) Universal set $A + \bar{A} = 1$.

10.3. Basic identities for logic variables

Relationships between logical variables are often very different to the usual arithmetical identities as Table 10.1 shows. The area A is considered to form a set with $\bar{A}$ such that

$$A + \bar{A} = 1, \tag{10.3}$$

i.e. $A + \bar{A}$ form a universal set as shown in Fig. 10.6b, from which the basic relationships given in Table 10.1 can be justified.

De Morgan's theorem. Referring to Fig. 10.5, the unshaded region is $\overline{A + B}$. This region is equivalent to the double shaded part of Fig. 10.7, which represents $\bar{A} \cdot \bar{B}$. (Positive slope shading

Table 10.1.

$A + 0 = A$	$A \cdot A = A$
$A \cdot 0 = 0$	$A + \bar{A} = 1$
$A + 1 = 1$	$A \cdot \bar{A} = 0$
$A \cdot 1 = A$	$\bar{\bar{A}} = A$
$A + A = A$	

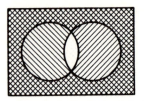

Fig. 10.7. Double-shaded region is $\bar{A} \cdot \bar{B}$. Total shaded region is $\bar{A} + \bar{B}$.

indicates $\bar{A}$, and negative slope $\bar{B}$.) There is thus the relationship

$$\overline{A + B} = \bar{A} \cdot \bar{B}. \tag{10.4}$$

Also, the unshaded part of Fig. 10.7 represents $A \cdot B$ which leaves the total shaded part as

$$\overline{A \cdot B} = \bar{A} + \bar{B}. \tag{10.5}$$

These relationships demonstrate *De Morgan's theorem* which can be stated as follows.

The negated AND (OR) function can be replaced by the OR (AND) function of the negated variables.

Inverted functions—NOR and NAND

The diode logic elements of Fig. 10.4 have current limitations which become apparent when further elements are connected. An inverting amplifier can be used to raise the current level. The OR and AND gates then perform NOT–OR and NOT–AND functions and are called NOR and NAND gates. As in Fig. 10.8a, the inverting operation is indicated by a circle at the output. The truth tables for the inverted functions are given in Fig. 10.4, where the output is shown in the right-hand column. For the NOR gate, the output is "1" only when the inputs are both zero, an AND type of operation. Similarly, for inverted inputs, the NAND gate performs an OR function. Since the inverted functions can each perform both AND and OR type operations, they are known as *universal decision elements*. Only one form of gate need be used as the basis of all combinational logic operations, and this is usually the NAND type.

Figure 10.8b shows that, using De Morgan's theorem, the NAND gate output is $\overline{A \cdot B} = \bar{A} + \bar{B}$. The same NAND gate can be represented by Fig. 10.8c, where the symbol is basically an OR type but has inverting circles at the inputs. To the right of the circles the inverted inputs become A and B, and the output is $A + B$, thus emphasizing the OR form of operation.

The basic NAND gate can be made from a diode AND gate and an inverting transistor amplifier as in Fig. 10.8d. The diode, between the gate and the transistor base, ensures that when the inputs are "0" the forward voltage of the input diodes does not bring the transistor into conduction. Figure 10.8e has the diodes replaced by an equivalent transistor structure with multiple emitters. The emitter–base junctions operate as input diodes, and the base–collector junction as the voltage level changing element.

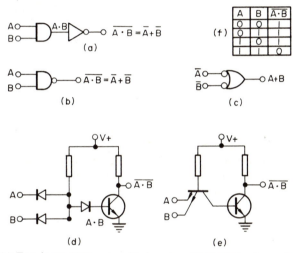

Fig. 10.8. (a) Two-input AND gate with inverter. (b) NAND gate symbol. (c) OR gate drawn with inverting inputs. (d) Diode–transistor NAND gate (DTL). (e) Transistor–transistor NAND gate (TTL). (f) Truth table.

10.4. Example—data handling

In Fig. 10.9, a two-position commutating switch directs digital data from either channel A or channel B to channel C. Switching is controlled by a variable X such that the A data is passed when $X =$ "1", and the B data is passed when $X =$ "0" ($\bar{X} =$ "1"). The logic expression is thus,

$$AX + B\bar{X} = C. \qquad (10.6)$$

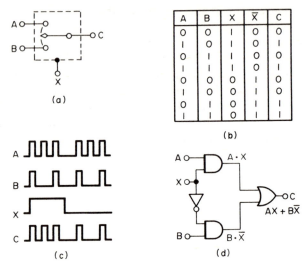

A	B	X	X̄	C
0	0	1	0	0
1	0	1	0	1
0	1	1	0	0
1	1	1	0	1
0	0	0	1	0
1	0	0	1	0
0	1	0	1	1
1	1	0	1	1

(b)

Fig. 10.9. Digital commutating switch.

The output C is "1" if A and X are each "1", or when B and $\bar{X}$ are "1". Since $X \cdot \bar{X} = 0$, X and $\bar{X}$ cannot simultaneously be "1" and either A or B, but never both, will be present at the output. The truth table and waveform diagrams are shown in Fig. 10.9. The logic expression shows that two AND gates and one OR gate are required, together with an inverter to provide $\bar{X}$. The same operation can be carried out using three NAND gates, as shown in Fig. 10.10a. From the output gate,

$$C = \overline{\overline{AX} \cdot \overline{B\bar{X}}} = \overline{\overline{AX}} \quad \overline{\overline{B\bar{X}}}, \quad \text{by De Morgan.}$$

Thus, $C = AX + B\bar{X}$, using a basic identity from Table 10.1. It is common practice to draw the symbols so that the inversion circles face each other as in Fig. 10.10b. The inversions cancel, and it is apparent that the output gate performs the OR function.

Digital multiplexer

The two input systems described above can be extended to a number of inputs, as shown in Fig. 10.11. The data channels A to D can be selected by making W to Z logic "1". This operation is

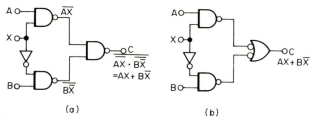

Fig. 10.10. Alternative forms of digital commuting switch. The arrangement of (b) emphasizes the *OR* operation of the output gate.

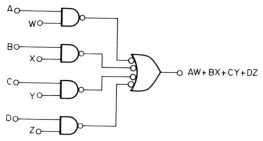

Fig. 10.11. Digital multiplexer. Channels A, B, C or D are selected by a "1" on W, X, Y or Z.

known as multiplexing and is frequently used in digital systems, often employing medium-scale integration, where all the elements are on a single substrate.

10.5.   Exclusive OR

Closely related to the commutating switch is the "exclusive-OR" function. This provides an output when one of the two inputs is zero, but not when both are zero, as is the case for the inclusive-OR gate of Fig. 10.4a. The basic logic statement for the exclusive-OR function is

$$A\bar{B} + \bar{A}B = C \qquad (10.7)$$

and, as shown in Fig. 10.12, requires two AND gates and one OR gate. The exclusive OR can also be formed from three NAND gates thus,

$$\overline{\overline{A\bar{B}} + \overline{\bar{A}B}} = \overline{\overline{A\bar{B}} \cdot \overline{\bar{A}B}}.$$

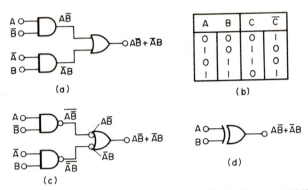

Fig. 10.12. Exclusive-OR function. The NAND form of (c) has its output NAND gate drawn as an OR with inverted inputs, and (d) gives the exclusive-OR symbol.

It is called a *modulo two adder* as the output is the sum of two numbers using a base of two.

Equivalence gate

The truth table given in Fig. 10.12b shows that the complement of an exclusive OR output is "1" when the inputs are equivalent, i.e. both "1", or both "0". This is demonstrated thus,

$$AB + \bar{A}\bar{B} = \overline{\overline{AB + \bar{A}\bar{B}}} = \overline{\overline{AB} \cdot \overline{\bar{A}\bar{B}}} = \overline{(\bar{A} + \bar{B}) \cdot (A + B)}$$

$$= \overline{A\bar{A} + A\bar{B} + \bar{A}B + B\bar{B}}$$

$$= \overline{A\bar{B} + \bar{A}B}, \quad \text{as } A\bar{A} = B\bar{B} = 0,$$

which is the complement of the exclusive OR relationship of eqn. (10.7).

10.6.   NAND bistable

If two NAND gates are coupled as in Fig. 10.13, they operate as a storage element, which remembers whether the last input was a "0" or "1". The outputs will usually be complementary except when both inputs are ones. The element is normally operated by a "1" on either the set or reset input. In the former case, the "0" at the input to the upper NAND gate ensures that the output becomes "1", and

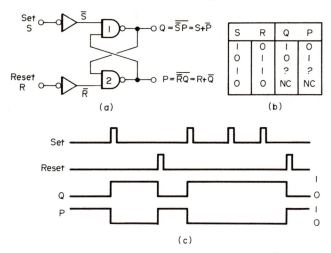

Fig. 10.13. (a) Set–reset bistable and its truth table (b). If both inputs remain at "0" there is no change in output (NC). (c) Output response to input pulses.

this forms one of the inputs to the lower NAND. As the other input is also "1", NAND 2 has "0" at the output. The NAND output is low (or "0") only when both inputs are high as shown in the truth table for the NAND in Fig. 10.8f. The "0" at the output of NAND 2 ensures that NAND 1 keeps its output high when the set input is removed. This is a stable state which is maintained until a reset pulse takes one input of NAND 2 low, making its output high. This in turn makes both inputs of NAND 1 high, bringing its output low, and forms the second stable state. Such a bistable is operated as in Fig. 10.13c, where a SET pulse switches the output to "1" and a subsequent RESET pulse returns the output to "0". An anomalous situation occurs when both SET and RESET pulses occur together. Both P and Q attempt to become high after the removal of the input pulses, and the output state is indeterminate.

10.7. Examples

(a) Voltage to frequency converter

A system is required to convert an input voltage to a square wave output which has a frequency proportional to the input voltage.

This is accomplished using the arrangement of Fig. 10.14a. The input voltage is applied to an integrator, the output voltage of which falls at a rate proportional to the applied voltage, until it reaches a specified value. At this point the sign of the input voltage is reversed and integration proceeds in the reverse direction until an upper limit is reached, at which point a further reversal occurs.

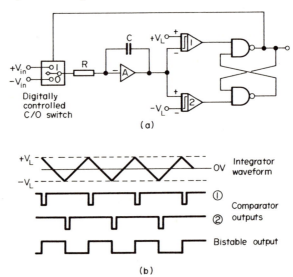

Fig. 10.14. (a) Basic voltage-to-frequency converter. The bistable stores the required state of the change-over switch. (b) Converter waveforms. The comparator outputs are normally high, becoming low when the integrator output reaches the limit voltage.

A bistable is used to indicate the direction in which the integration should go. It is operated by two comparators with upper and lower limit voltages applied to the appropriate inputs. When the inegrator output exceeds the limit voltage the comparator output switches from a "1" to a "0". The NAND having one input low, will provide a "1" at the input of the other NAND. This provides a further low input to the first NAND, which will then remain in the high state after the trigger pulse from the comparator is removed. The output from the bistable controls the analogue switch, keeping the integrator operating between the limit voltages. The bistable also provides the square wave output, which has a frequency proportional to the input voltage.

Frequency

For the integrator with a constant input voltage V_{in} the output voltage

$$v_o = -\frac{V_{in}}{CR}t, \quad \text{from eqn. (6.35)}$$

where t is the period of integration.

In this example the output voltage is limited to the range between the reference voltages, i.e. $2V_L$, and the time of integration,

$$t = \frac{2V_L CR}{V_{in}}. \tag{10.8}$$

As t represents only half a cycle, the frequency is given by

$$f = \frac{1}{2t} = \frac{V_{in}}{4V_L CR}. \tag{10.9}$$

Figure 10.15 shows a voltage to frequency converter which uses only one logic-controlled analogue switch. These devices usually operate most satisfactorily at a summing point, where the voltage is limited and the device is switching current.

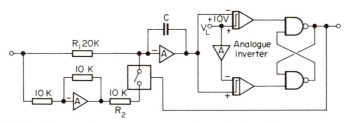

Fig. 10.15. Voltage-to-frequency converter using a single-position analogue switch. Amplifiers should have non-inverting inputs connected to ground by 10 kΩ resistors.

Design considerations

Resistor selection. For an equal mark–space ratio, the "on" resistance of the digitally controlled analogue switch should be very much less than R_2. A value of 10 kΩ will be approximately 100 times the switch resistance. R_2 has half the resistance of R_1, and will supply twice the current, thus reversing the effective current at the amplifier summing point when the switch is operated.

Capacitor selection. The minimum value for R, as indicated above, is usually the most satisfactory for amplifier operation, always providing that the resulting capacitor value is not excessive. Using the resistor values given in Fig. 10.15, and assuming the maximum frequency for $V_{in} = 10$ V is to be 10 kHz, from eqn. (10.9),

$$C = \frac{V_{in}}{4 V_L R f} = \frac{10 \text{ V}}{4 \times 10 \text{ V} \times 20 \times 10^3 \times 10^3}$$

$$= 0.0125 \ \mu\text{F}. \tag{10.10}$$

(b) *Variable mark–space generator*

If in the system of Fig. 10.14a the $- V_{in}$ terminal is connected to a negative reference voltage, the output voltage will have a variable mark–space ratio as shown in Fig. 10.16. The period τ_1 is constant and τ_2 is inversely proportional to V_{in}.

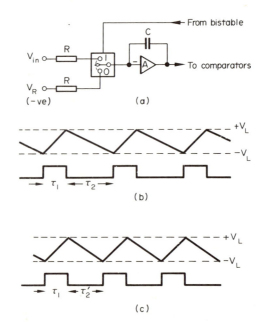

Fig. 10.16. A variable mark–space system. (a) The switch connects either V_{in} or V_R to the amplifier input. (b) Waveforms for integrator and bistable (NAND gate 2 output). (c) Waveforms for larger input voltage.

Thus

$$\tau_1 = \frac{2V_L CR}{V_R} \quad \text{and} \quad \tau_2 = \frac{2V_L CR}{V_{in}},$$

or

$$\frac{\tau_1}{\tau_2} = \frac{V_{in}}{V_R}.$$

(c) Variable pulse-width modulator

A pulse-width modulator, with the mean output proportional to the input voltage, is formed by keeping the input voltage permanently connected to the integrator and switching the reference voltage as in Fig. 10.17a.

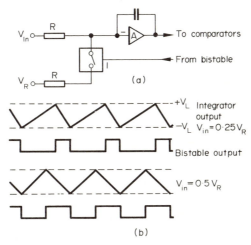

Fig. 10.17. Modification of Fig. 10.14a to provide a pulse waveform of mean value proportional to input voltage. (b) Waveforms for two values of input voltage.

Then

$$\tau_1 = \frac{2V_L CR}{V_{in}} \quad \text{and} \quad \tau_2 = \frac{2V_L CR}{V_R - V_{in}},$$

or

$$\frac{\tau_1}{\tau_2} = \frac{V_R - V_{in}}{V_{in}} \quad \text{and} \quad \frac{\tau_2}{\tau_1 + \tau_2} = \frac{V_{in}}{V_R}. \tag{10.11}$$

The mean area of the pulse is proportional to the input voltage, V_{in}, as shown in Fig. 10.17b.

10.8. Clocked bistable

If the inverters associated with the bistables shown in Fig. 10.13 are replaced by two NAND gates, as in Fig. 10.18, the transitions take place only when the clock pulse is high.

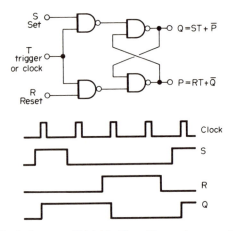

Fig. 10.18. Clocked set–reset bistable. Transitions only occur at clock pulses.

Data input bistable

The bistable of Fig. 10.19 uses an inverter to ensure that complementary inputs are applied to the input NAND gates. The indeterminate state when the inputs are both "1" is not possible with this arrangement, and the outputs will always be complementary, Q being high when the D input is high. The Q output follows the data which is present at the input at the time of the clock pulse.

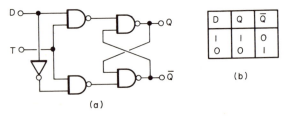

D	Q	$\bar{Q}$
I	I	O
O	O	I

(b)

(a)

Fig. 10.19. Data input bistable. Output Q follows input D at each clock pulse. The two outputs are always complementary.

10.9. Delta modulator

This provides a pulse waveform which approximates to the rate of change of an analogue input signal. It has applications in digital data systems, and has the form shown in Fig. 10.20.

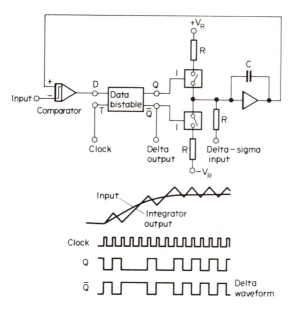

Fig. 10.20. Delta modulator.

The output from the integrator is compared with the analogue input signal. If the latter is greater, the comparator output is low (logic "0") and on the application of a clock pulse, the $\bar{Q}$ output of the bistable will be "1". This closes the switch to the $-V_R$ supply causing the integrator output to move in a positive direction, bringing it closer to the analogue input. When this voltage is reached, on the next clock pulse the bistable will change its state and integration will proceed in the reverse direction. In this manner, the integrator output follows the analogue input and, since the integrator input is the bistable waveform, the latter represents the derivative of the analogue input.

An alternative form of operation uses the delta–sigma input

shown in Fig. 10.20, and in this case the comparator inverting input is grounded. The resulting output is a clocked pulse-width modulation. The integrator averages the difference between the pulse waveform and the analogue input, and the comparator output directs the bistable to the state which reduces the difference between the two waveforms. The delta–sigma output is consequently a pulse approximation of the analogue input.

Design considerations

If values of $R = 10 \, k\Omega$ and $V_R = \pm 10 \, V$ are assumed, the only design value is for C, the integrator capacitor. For a clock frequency of 1 kHz, if the maximum integrator change during each clock period is limited to 0.1 V (i.e. 1 per cent of 10 V full output), the appropriate value of C is found from the relationship for an integrator with constant input voltage V_R.

$$V_o = -\frac{t V_R}{CR} \quad \text{or} \quad C = \left|\frac{t V_R}{V_o R}\right| = \frac{10 \times 10^{-3}}{10^{-1} \times 10^4} = 10 \, \mu F.$$

As the rate of change of a sine wave, $E \sin \omega t$, is

$$\frac{d}{dt} E \sin \omega t = E\omega \cos \omega t,$$

with maximum value $E\omega$, the above rate of change of the integrator output 0.1 V in 1 ms (i.e. V/s), will limit the frequency which the modulator can handle to

$$\omega = \frac{100 \, V/s}{E} = 10 \, r/s \quad \text{for} \quad E = 10 \, V.$$

If higher frequencies are to be handled, a smaller C is required, with a higher clock rate to reduce the "noise".

10.10. Master–slave JK bistable

Two clocked RS bistables can be coupled to provide bistable operation which has an output conditional on the JK inputs, with no indeterminate states. The master bistable, as shown in Fig. 10.21, operates on the application of the clock.

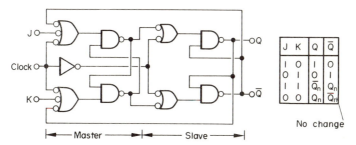

J	K	Q	Q̄
1	0	1	0
0	1	0	1
1	1	$\bar{Q}_n$	Q_n
0	0	Q_n	$\bar{Q}_n$

No change

Fig. 10.21. (a) Master–slave JK bistable (flip-flop). The master is set when the clock is high and its state is transferred to the slave when the clock goes low. (b) Truth table. States shown after the application of the $(n + 1)$th clock pulse.

If both the J and K inputs are present, the high output will direct the clock pulse through the input gate to which it is connected. This will set the NAND of the master. When the clock subsequently falls to a "0", the slave input NAND transfers the "1" to the output NAND which was previously a "0". A further clock pulse will be redirected to the other output. The bistable, or flip-flop, thus "toggles", the outputs changing from "0" to "1" and back to "0" with the application of successive clock pulses. The two output states enable the flip-flop to count in a binary manner. If both J and K are kept at "0", the flip-flop cannot change state as the clock pulses are gated at the input NAND gates. When either J or K is high the flip-flop is set or reset by the clock and will remain in that state as subsequent clock pulses will be directed along the same path.

10.11. Flip-flop binary counters

(a) *Asynchronous operation*

Figure 10.22 shows how four bistables can be connected to provide a counter with sixteen distinct states. The waveforms are drawn for *edge triggered* bistables which operate on the rising edge of the clock waveform. Master–slave flip-flops could be used but, because the slave is not operated until the clock waveform goes low, appear to operate on the negative edge.

A *clear* input resets all the flip-flops to "0", independent of the

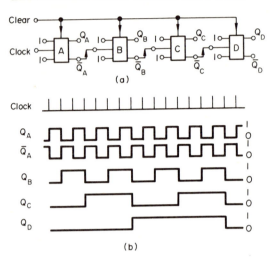

Fig. 10.22. Asynchronous counter. (a) Bistable connections. (b) Waveforms for positive edge-triggered bistables.

trigger input, and sometimes a *set* input is available which will set the devices to "1".

This type of counter is often referred to as a *ripple through*, as each bistable is triggered by the preceding one. Since each flip-flop requires a finite time for operation a long counter might require an unacceptable time to operate, if all the bistables are being toggled. This is particularly so where the counter is being used in the *up–down* mode, the counting is reversed by changing the trigger inputs from the $\bar{Q}$ output to the Q output. Time must be allowed for the trigger pulse to propagate through, before the reversing connections are made. Each stage could require 50 nS propagation time, ten stages consequently taking 500 nS. Thus the counting rate would be limited to 2 MHz.

(b) *Synchronous operation*

This provides a faster method of counting. When the trigger pulses are all applied in parallel to the flip-flops, as in Fig. 10.23, it is necessary to arrange the gating of the *JK* inputs so that only the required elements are switched. The gating is set up before the trigger is applied. The first stage, *A*, always toggles so its *JK* inputs are kept high. From Fig. 10.22 it is apparent that *B* is required to

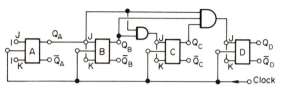

Fig. 10.23. Synchronous counter. Clock pulses are applied to all the stages, but a flip-flop can operate only when the preceding ones are high.

change when Q_A is high. Likewise C changes when Q_A and Q_B are high. Flip-flop C must have its JK inputs controlled by an AND gate with inputs Q_A and Q_B. Likewise D derives its JK inputs from an AND gate having Q_A, Q_B and Q_C as inputs. With this arrangement the propagation time is reduced to the operating time for the AND gates, together with the switching time for one bistable, and is independent of the number of stages in the counter.

10.12. Decoding

The sixteen states of a four-stage counter (representing numbers 0 to 15) are given by combinations of the states of the individual bistables. These are shown in Fig. 10.24a.

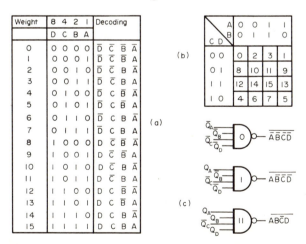

Fig. 10.24. States of a four-stage binary counter. (a) Q outputs corresponding to Fig. 10.23, and decoding connections, $A = Q_A$ and $\bar{A} = \bar{Q}_A$. (b) Karnaugh map showing all possible combinations of A, B, C and D. (c) NAND decoding. The output is low when all inputs are high.

Alternatively the states can be plotted as a *Karnaugh map* shown in Fig. 10.24b. All the possible states of the four bistables are arranged as axes, and the counting numbers inserted at the appropriate positions.

Four-input gates can be used to provide a unique indication of the state. As shown in Fig. 10.24c, the appropriate selection of the bistable outputs when combined in an AND gate will give a high output for only one input combination. The required combinations are found from the complements of the "0" together with the "1"s from Fig. 10.24a.

Thus for 0 (zero) the complementary outputs $\bar{Q}_A$, $\bar{Q}_B$, $\bar{Q}_C$ and $\bar{Q}_D$ provide an output "1". Similarly for 10 (ten) the required combination is $\bar{Q}$, Q_B, $\bar{Q}_C$ and Q_D. All the combinations are listed in Fig. 10.24b.

10.13. Decade counter

By decoding the eleventh state (i.e. count of 10) and using this to reset the flip-flops, the count will be restricted to the range 0 to 9. This arrangement is shown in Fig. 10.25a. If the states are to be

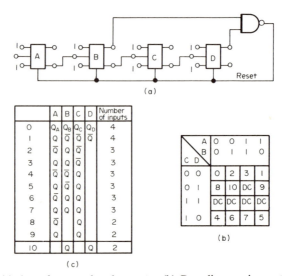

(a)

	A	B	C	D	Number of inputs
0	Q_A	Q_B	Q_C	Q_D	4
1	Q	$\bar{Q}$	$\bar{Q}$	$\bar{Q}$	4
2	$\bar{Q}$	Q	$\bar{Q}$		3
3	Q	Q	$\bar{Q}$		3
4	$\bar{Q}$	$\bar{Q}$	Q		3
5	Q	$\bar{Q}$	Q		3
6	$\bar{Q}$	Q	Q		3
7	Q	Q	Q		3
8	$\bar{Q}$		Q		2
9	Q		Q		2
10		Q		Q	2

(c)

	A	0	0	1	1
C D	B	0	1	1	0
0 0		0	2	3	1
0 1		8	10	DC	9
1 1		DC	DC	DC	DC
1 0		4	6	7	5

(b)

Fig. 10.25. (a) Asynchronous decade counter. (b) Decoding requirements. The tenth position is sensed by the gate and immediately resets the counter to zero. (c) Karnaugh map with "Don't Care" states indicated (DC). 10 is a DC state for counting but is used for resetting to zero.

decoded, four-input gates are not necessarily required in all positions, as the binary states 11 to 15 will not be occupied. If 10 is used to reset the counter it is not necessary to distinguish it from its neighbour 11, which will be an unoccupied state. Thus the output from flip-flop *A* of Fig. 10.25a is not required. Similiarly, as 14 is unoccupied, *C* which distinguishes it from 10 is not required. Therefore 10 can be decoded with a two-input gate as shown. The method of reduction is to examine the immediate neighbours on Fig. 10.25b, and observe whether it is necessary for them to be separated. For 0, its neighbours are 1, 4, 2 and 8. (The boundaries are continuous, 1 being to the left of 0 and 0 being to the right of 1.) As these must all be separately displayed, a 4 input gate is necessary, as is also the case for 1. However, 2 has neighbours 0, 6, 3 and 10 and as the latter is not displayed, *D* is not required. The complete decoding requirements are given in Fig. 10.25c.

10.14.   Counter applications

(a) *Digital voltmeter*

Figure 10.26 shows a system in which pulses are passed through an AND gate until the ramp output from an integrator exceeds the

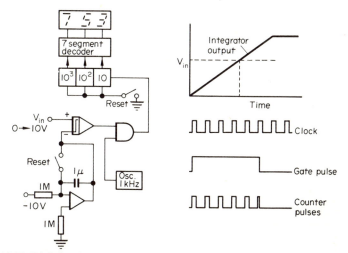

Fig. 10.26. Digital voltmeter and associated waveforms. Operation begins when the two-pole reset switch is opened.

input voltage. The number held in the counter is proportional to the input voltage.

Design considerations

An input voltage, nominally 0 to 10 V is to be represented by three digits, i.e. 0 to 9.99. Let the oscillator frequency be 1 kHz and the time required to fill the counter 1 s.

Integrator time constant. The integrator output should reach the maximum input voltage of 10 V in 1 s, which consequently is the required time constant. Make $R = 1$ MΩ and $C = 1$ μF.

Reset switch. This is a double-pole switch which resets the counter to zero (000) and discharges the integrator capacitor.

Counter and display unit. The most convenient, as well as the most economical, method of counting is to use integrated decade units (medium scale integrated devices, *MSI*). Typical of such is the SN 7490, a four-stage counter consisting of a divide by two stage followed by a divide by five stage. The schematic of the Texas SN 7490N, a dual-in-line version, is given in Fig. 10.27, together with truth tables for (b) the count sequence, and (c) the reset/count requirements. When used as a binary coded decimal counter (*BCD*), output A is connected to input BD, and for a three-decade system three such devices are cascaded.

A convenient form of numerical read-out is the seven-segment display. As shown in Fig. 10.26, the counter output can be converted into a numerical display by the use of a seven-segment decoder such as the SN 7448.

Automatic operation. The system provides a reading when the reset switch is released. If it is modified as in Fig. 10.28, a new reading will be provided every 10 s. The four-stage counter will cycle each 10-s period and the most significant stage will have its fourth bit high, i.e. "1", for the final 2 s. This "high" is used to reset the display counter, and operate a logic controlled switch to reset the integrator.

Latching operation. To prevent the display changing during the counting operation, the final count can be held on latches. These are essentially cross-coupled gates which retain the input state at the instant when the trigger goes from high to low. If the most significant decade of the control counter is decoded to provide an output at the fifth state (i.e. an AND gate with inputs Q_A, $\bar{Q}_B$, Q_C) the display will

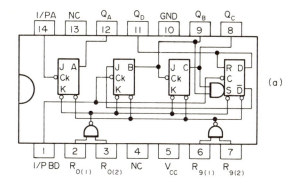

(a)

Count	Q_D	Q_C	Q_B	Q_A
0	0	0	0	0
1	0	0	0	1
2	0	0	1	0
3	0	0	1	1
4	0	1	0	0
5	0	1	0	1
6	0	1	1	0
7	0	1	1	1
8	1	0	0	0
9	1	0	0	1

(b)

Resets inputs				Outputs
$R_{0(1)}$	$R_{0(2)}$	$R_{9(1)}$	$R_{9(2)}$	D C B A
1	1	0	X	0 0 0 0
1	1	X	0	0 0 0 0
X	X	1	1	1 0 0 1
X	0	X	0	Count
0	X	0	X	Count
0	X	X	0	Count
X	0	0	X	Count

X = Don't care

(c)

Fig. 10.27. SN 7490N BCD counter and its truth tables; (b) gives the counting sequence and (c) the reset/count states.

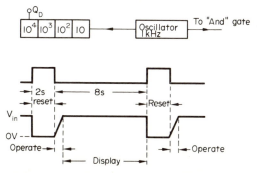

Fig. 10.28. A four-decade counter gives the reset waveform for automatic operation of the digital voltmeter.

change to the new reading without any flicker. This is illustrated in Fig. 10.29.

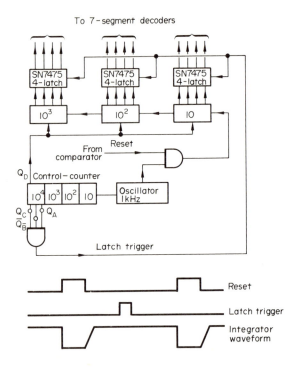

Fig. 10.29. Display blinking is eliminated by the use of latches.

(b) *Analogue to digital converter*

The output of the latch is a digital representation of the current sample of the input voltage. It can be in binary coded decimal form as before, ranging from 0 to 999, or pure binary which for twelve stages would range from 0 to 4095. If latches are used, the display period (Fig. 10.28) can be reduced to speed up operation. A higher frequency clock could also be used.

(c) *Period measurement*

The system shown in Fig. 10.26 is basically a period measuring device. Figure 10.30 shows how the period of an input waveform can

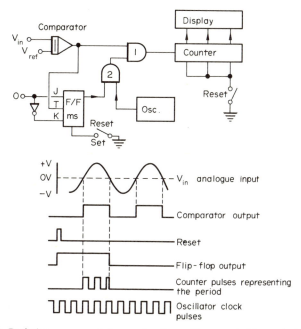

Fig. 10.30. Period measurement. In practice the oscillator period is much shorter than the measured period.

be measured. The comparator squares the input signal, thus converting an analogue input into pulse form which, when high, allows the oscillator pulses to be counted. The master–slave *JK* flip-flop is reset to "0" when the comparator output returns to zero. This prevents further pulses being counted if a subsequent positive input is present. Initially the flip-flop is set manually and the counter is cleared using a manual switch. The system is then ready for the analogue input; when this is greater than zero the comparator output is high and AND gate 1 passes the oscillator pulses. As the gating waveform falls to zero, the flip-flop is reset and no further oscillator pulses will reach AND gate 1. The counter now holds the number of pulses passed during the period in which the analogue input was greater than zero, and this is retained until the system is manually reset. Automatic operation can be introduced using techniques similar to those described for the digital voltmeter.

(d) *Frequency measurement*

By counting the number of pulses present in a period of known duration, the frequency of the pulse waveform can be determined. If, using the system shown in Fig. 10.31, 800 pulses were counted during a counting period of 1 s, the frequency would be 800 Hz. Greater precision could be obtained if a longer counting period was used, together with more counter and display stages.

Thus, if the timing oscillator frequency is 1.25 kHz, and it is divided by 10^3 by the three-decade counter as shown, reference to the truth table of Fig. 10.27b indicates that in the third stage $\bar{Q}_D$ during periods 0 to 7 provides a counting period of 1 s. The latching period (8) is obtained from $Q_D \cdot \bar{Q}_A$, and the reset period (9) by gating $Q_D \cdot Q_A$, and both will be of 0.125 s duration. The display changes only at the leading edge of the latching pulse, when the counter state is transferred to the display. As before, the comparator is used to convert sinusoidal waveforms into rectangular pulse form.

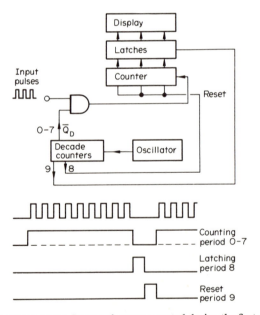

Fig. 10.31. Frequency meter. Input pulses are counted during the first eight states of the most significant decade of the oscillator counter. The remaining two states are used for latching the display and resetting.

(e) *Integrating digital voltmeter*

Figure 10.15 shows a voltage to frequency converter which is based on an input integrator. The output of this device can be combined with a frequency counter to form a digital voltmeter. One advantage of this system, over the previously described form, is that 50 Hz noise does not affect the measurement if the integration period is a multiple of 20 ms.

CHAPTER 11

Some General Design Considerations

In this chapter consideration is given to some general aspects of electronic design practice which are applicable to all the preceding chapters. Subjects dealt with include the factors influencing the choice of resistors and capacitors, and guidance on the use of integrated circuits. The chapter is concluded with some notes on screening and earths.

11.1. Resistors[55]

The main characteristics to be considered in selecting a resistor for a given application are size, wattage rating, stability and tolerance. There are in addition, noise, maximum operating voltage and frequency range each of which may also be of importance in special cases.

Wattage rating

This specifies the maximum amount of power which may be dissipated in a component without excessive rise in temperature, and is usually stated for operation in an ambient temperature up to 40°C. Where the ambient temperature is in excess of this figure, the component should be derated in accordance with the manufacturer's derating curves. Typically, a component rated at 40°C might have its maximum permissible dissipation reduced by 50 per cent when used in an ambient of 70°C. It is good design practice to operate carbon resistors at 60 per cent of their rated value.

Stability

This is an indication of the ability of a resistor to retain its stated value during a reasonable period of storage and also throughout its useful life. It is not possible to give a simple figure of merit for the stability of a resistor because of the different characteristics which affect it. Instead, a manufacturer will usually indicate the limit of resistance change, stated as a percentage of the original value, which may be expected, as follows.

Load change is the maximum permitted change after 1000 hours operation in an ambient of 70°C at the full wattage dissipation of the resistor.

Temperature coefficient of resistance of a component indicates the change of resistance as a function of operating temperature, stated as so many parts per 10^6 per °C.

Voltage coefficient of resistance applies only to carbon composition resistors and indicates a decrease in resistance value which may be expected as an applied d.c. voltage is increased.

In addition to these three, the limits of resistance change after 1 year storage and when the component is soldered are also usually stated.

Tolerance

Stated as a percentage of the resistance of the component, this indicates the maximum and minimum values which may be expected of a component having a given nominal resistance. Resistors are available having tolerances of ±20, ±10, ±5, ±2 and ±1 per cent and a designer should anticipate that the majority of components will have values which lie close to the two limits.

Preferred values

Resistors are manufactured in a range of preferred values such that any resistor plus its tolerance is approximately equal in value to the next larger resistor minus its tolerance. These preferred values are given in Table 11.1.

Table 11.1 Preferred resistor values.

10**	16	27	43	68**
11	18*	30	47**	75
12*	20	33**	51	82*
13	22**	36	56*	91
15**	24	39*	62	100**

Resistors are commonly available in multiples of ten of the stated values, between 10 Ω and 10 MΩ. The complete list of Table 11.1 is available in 5 per cent components. Those marked with one asterisk are supplied in 5 and 10 per cent tolerances, while those with two asterisks are obtainable in 5, 10 and 20 per cent.

Colour Code

Figure 11.1 illustrates a method by which the value of a resistor can be identified using a standard colour code, as follows:

0 — Black	5 — Green
1 — Brown	6 — Blue
2 — Red	7 — Violet
3 — Orange	8 — Grey
4 — Yellow	9 — White

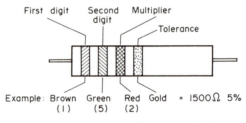

Fig. 11.1. Use of the resistor colour code. The "multiplier" band determines the number of zeros which follow the second digit.

Each resistor carries four bands of colour. The first and second bands indicate the first two digits of the resistance value, and the number of zeros which follow is specified by the colour of the third band. The fourth colour indicates the tolerance of the component as a percentage, as follows, brown—1, red—2, gold—5 and silver—10. Thus, a resistor having the colour yellow, violet, orange and gold, in that order, is a 5 per cent component of 47 kΩ resistance.

Alternatively, resistors are identified by a legend printed on them, which makes use of an alphabetic code. In this, the multipliers K and M are used to define the position of a decimal point, i.e. 2.7 kΩ is written as 2K7 and 1.5 MΩ is written as 1M5. The letter R is used as a decimal point at the beginning or end of a number and the percentage tolerances 1, 2, 5, 10 and 20 are represented by the letters *F*, *G*, *J*, *K* and *M* respectively. Thus,

$$100RF = 100 \, \Omega \pm 1 \text{ per cent}$$
$$1K2J = 1.2 \, k\Omega \pm 5 \text{ per cent}$$
$$2M2M = 2.2 \, M\Omega \pm 20 \text{ per cent}$$

11.2.   Resistor types

Carbon composition

These are the cheapest resistors available. Stability generally is poor and the resistance may change several per cent during lengthy periods of storage, and by as much as 10 per cent through the normal life of the resistor. In addition to thermal agitation noise, which is present in all resistive elements, the composition resistor generates extra noise when current is flowing through it. This fact is of serious importance in such specialized applications as are found, for instance, in the medical electronic field where requirements often couple high gain with low noise.

Carbon film

Typically, a ceramic former is coated with a crystallized carbon film deposit which forms the resistance element. Components are available in the range $2.2 \, \Omega$ to $1 \, M\Omega$ with 5 and 10 per cent tolerances and power ratings between 0.2 W and 2 W. Although they are a little more expensive, they are replacing composition types for general purpose use, because of their inherent low noise and better stability.

Metal oxide

This is another "film" resistor, but in this case the deposition is of tin oxide instead of carbon. As with the carbon film component, the final ohmic value is achieved by cutting a spiral through to the ceramic base, thus increasing the effective path length between the ends of the resistor, and thus increasing the resistance. If the resistor ohmic value is monitored as the spiral groove is formed it is possible to obtain a final value within ± 0.1 per cent of the required value.

As a means of comparison, typical specification limits for these three types of resistors are given in Table 11.2.[56]

Table 11.2 Typical resistor specification limits.

	Composition	Carbon-film	Metal oxide
Load change	±15%	±3%	±3%
Temperature coefficient (ppm/°C)	±1200	−800	±250
Voltage coefficient	−0.05%/V	Zero	Zero
Noise (μV/V)	$2 + \log 0.001R$	0.5	1.0

Metal film

For use as emitter resistors in transistor output stages, resistance values of less than $10\,\Omega$ are frequently necessary. Metal film resistors can be used for this purpose. They have the advantage that relatively large amounts of power can be dissipated in small components. Typically, a nickel film resistor has a load stability within ±3 per cent, with negligible voltage coefficient and noise, and a positive temperature coefficient in the range 0 to 600 ppm/°C.

Wirewound resistors

These are manufactured with either ordinary or non-inductive windings and are used where even greater stability is desired, or where it is necessary to dissipate more power than is possible with other types. Wirewound resistors will dissipate up to 100 W, depending on their size, but due to the type of construction used the maximum value normally encountered is of the order of 50 kΩ. These resistors operate with high surface temperatures and should be sited so as to ensure adequate ventilation and to avoid damage to adjacent components.

11.3. Capacitors[57]

Capacitors are characterized by their stability, tolerance, working voltage, dielectric absorption, leakage current, insulation resistance and power factor. The first two of these characteristics have the same significance, referred to the value of capacitance, as was stated in § 11.1 for resistors.

Working voltage

This indicates the maximum voltage to which the capacitor should be subjected in normal use. It is commonly given for both d.c. and a.c. conditions and is valid over a given range of ambient temperatures. Where the stated ambient is exceeded, the working voltage should be suitably derated.

Both working voltage and temperature influence the expected life of a capacitor. In some types, operation at a temperature 10°C higher than the permitted maximum results in a reduction in life of 50 per cent. Operation of capacitors at voltages much less than the stated maximum extends the life of the component significantly; an important consideration when designing equipment for which a high degree of reliability is required.

Dielectric absorption

If a fully charged capacitor is momentarily discharged, and then left open circuited, a further charge will build up in the component due to the energy absorbed by the dielectric during the charging process. The phenomenon is known as dielectric absorption and results in a reduction in capacitance as frequency is increased. It also introduces undesirable time lags in pulse and high-speed switching circuits.

Leakage resistance

When a capacitor is charged from a d.c. source and the source is then removed, the charge will not be held indefinitely but will leak away due to the flow of leakage currents. The effect is as if the capacitor was shunted by a resistance, and the time a given component takes to discharge to 36.8 per cent of its initial charge is usually given as a CR time constant. Leakage currents increase with temperature and are of significance where the capacitor is used to couple two points of different d.c. potential.

Insulation resistance

This is an indication of the effective series resistance of a capacitor, and since it varies with capacitance, again a figure of ohms-farads is quoted. Where a capacitor is to be shunted by a high value resistance to provide a given time constant, the effect of insulation resistance on the resulting time constant should be considered. Such a requirement is often met in servomechanisms when stabilization is to be achieved by the use of passive networks.

Power factor

When an alternating current flows in a capacitor the current leads the voltage by an angle somewhat less than the ideal 90°. The power factor of a component is the cosine of this phase angle and for a perfect capacitor equals zero. The power factor may also be defined as the ratio of power wasted per cycle to useful power per cycle. It is a function of applied voltage and determines the capacitor internal heating.

11.4.   Capacitor types

Capacitors are most conveniently grouped according to the dielectric used. Only the more commonly encountered types are here discussed.

Ceramic

These may be divided into two groups according to their permittivities and temperature coefficients. The first group having low permittivity, low loss and precise temperature coefficients find typical use in tuned circuits of radio receivers for temperature-compensating purposes. Those having permittivities in excess of 500 generally provide less stability with changes in temperature, having higher losses and lower d.c. working voltage than the low permittivity types. They are only suitable for working with small a.c. voltages and are used mainly as r.f. bypass capacitors. Values up to 0.015 μF are commonly available with tolerances of $\pm 20\%$.

Mica

Mica is a dielectric which provides high stability and low loss, and enables capacitors to be made with small capacitance tolerances. Working voltages are generally in excess of 300 V and insulation resistance is in the range 3000–6000 MΩ. Where good long-term stability is required silvered mica components may be used. They exhibit very small changes in value at frequencies up to several megaherz and are often used in v.h.f. intermediate frequency transformers. Mica capacitors have very low power factors and are available with 5, 10 and 20 per cent tolerances and values ranging from 33 pF to 0.01 μF.

Polystyrene

The main advantages of the polystyrene capacitor are its low dielectric absorption, excellent power factor and very high insulation resistance which varies little with changes in temperature, enabling it to be used in long time constant circuits. This type of capacitor is extensively used in the analogue computing field. Its main disadvantage is the maximum temperature at which it should be used. This should not normally exceed 60°C.

Polyester

These are low-cost components with high insulation resistance, but whose dielectric absorption is worse than that of polystyrene.

Impregnated paper

These are relatively cheap general-purpose capacitors providing high capacitance to volume ratios and capable of working at reasonably high d.c. voltages. Single units in tubular form are manufactured in values between 0.001 and 1.0 μF, generally having ±20 per cent tolerance. Irrespective of the d.c. working voltages, the maximum a.c. working voltage for a single unit is normally about 300 V r.m.s. at 50 Hz. Insulation resistance varies according to the impregnant used and decreases with increasing temperature. The power factor of impregnated paper capacitors is in the range 0.005–0.01 at 1 kHz and increases with frequency. Stability is normally of the order of 1–5 per cent.

Metallized paper

The use of metallized paper results in a smaller component for a given capacitance, and has the advantage that dielectric punctures caused by the application of excessive voltages are self-healing. Insulation resistance, however, is much less than that of impregnated-paper types. They are commonly used for decoupling h.f. and i.f. circuits where the main requirement is that of low impedance. The power factor of a metallized paper capacitor is about 0.02 at 1 kHz and capacitance stability is normally between 5 and 10 per cent.

Electrolytic capacitors

These have a higher capacitance–volume ratio than any other capacitor, particularly at low working voltages, but they may only be used in circuit positions where they are subjected to substantially direct voltage. The capacitors must be connected correctly with regard to polarity and are extensively used as a.f. bypass and smoothing components. When used for smoothing in power supply circuits, care must be taken to ensure that not only is the maximum ripple voltage not exceeded, but also that the d.c. voltage plus peak ripple voltage is less than the voltage rating of the component. The maximum rated voltage for electrolytic capacitors rarely exceeds 500 V and is commonly made much less; 6 and 12 V ratings are readily available. When operated at the stated working voltage, leakage current is fairly high and increases with temperature. The operation of normal type electrolytic capacitors in high ambient temperatures and in the presence of large a.c. voltages tends to reduce their service life. These conditions should therefore be avoided in the interests of reliability. Where high ambient temperatures are expected, tantalum electrolytic capacitors may be employed. These generally have lower leakage current than the normal type and are extremely small. Ratings are available between 2.5 and 25 V which makes them suitable for use in transistor circuits. Electrolytic capacitors generally have very wide tolerances, $-20\% +100\%$ being typical.

11.5.   Practical use of TTL devices[58]

The widespread use of series 74 digital logic has led to the formulation of guidelines to assist in design with such devices. Some of these are stated here for ease of reference.

General

It is recommended that the $+5$-V power supply be obtained from a power unit having better than 5 per cent regulation, less than 5 per cent ripple and with the primary winding of its transformer bypassed for r.f. Where a large number of devices are mounted on one printed circuit board, V_{CC} should be decoupled every five packages with an r.f. capacitor; a suitable value for this purpose is 0.047 μF. Additionally, where possible, a *ground plane* should be provided. This requires the use of double-sided p.c. board, one side of which is devoted to the circuit interconnections. The other side, on which the components are mounted, has holes drilled in the copper to provide clearance around the component connections, and is then connected to earth. Where a ground plane is not possible, it is good practice to provide a grounded strip, as wide as possible, around the periphery of the p.c. board, with both ends of the strip taken to ground at a common point.

Unused inputs

As a general rule, no device input should be left "floating". Providing that it does not cause the fan-out capability of a driving device to be exceeded, an unused input to a gate may be connected to another used input. Where this is not possible, Fig. 11.2 illustrates two methods of tying down unused inputs of AND and NAND gates.

(a) Tie to V_{CC} through a 1-kΩ resistor. Several unused inputs may be tied by the same resistor.

(c) Tie to the output of an unused gate, whose input is tied to ground.

In any case, the inputs of an unused gate should be earthed as this is the condition for minimum power drain. The methods used for AND and NAND gates are also suitable for tying down unused *clear* and *preset* inputs of flip-flop devices.

Unused inputs of NOR gates should be tied to ground.

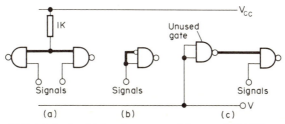

Fig. 11.2. Methods of tying down unused inputs of NAND gates.

Pulses

For a source impedance greater than 100 Ω, the rise time of a gate input pulse should not exceed 1 μs and the pulse length should be not less than 30 ns. For clock pulses for flip-flops, it is recommended that rise and fall times should not exceed 150 ns. In general, while a clock pulse is high, the input data of a *J–K* master–slave device should not be changed, and preset and clear pulses should be maintained.

Interconnections

Single wires up to 25 cm in length may be used without taking any special precautions. Above this length, however, a ground plane is essential with the wire being run as close as possible to the plane. Above 50 cm, the use of twisted pair or coaxial connectors is recommended with design being centred on lines of 100 Ω characteristic impedance.

11.6. Screening[59]

When an electric current flows in a conductor electromagnetic energy is radiated, the magnitude of which is a function of the amplitude and frequency of the current. Any conductor situated within the radiated field will have some of this energy induced in it, and thus undesirable coupling between different parts of a circuit may result. It is sometimes possible to mitigate this effect by arranging that equal and opposite self-cancelling voltages are induced. This is the principle which dictates that conductors carrying alternating current should be twisted together. The method is effective up to 5 kHz and the effectiveness depends to a large extent on the uniformness and tightness of the twist employed. The adequate separation of the component parts of a circuit from a radiating source will also reduce pick-up since, at a distance, the flux density will be reduced. Where, however, such methods are ineffective, an attempt must be made to contain the radiated field by means of a conducting screen and the following notes are intended as a guidance to this end.

Selection of screening materials

The effectiveness of a conducting screen in reducing the energy of an electromagnetic wave is the result of two effects.

(a) Absorption loss as the wave passes through the conducting medium.

(b) Reflection loss occurring at each surface of discontinuity.

Both are frequency dependent and are also affected by the nature of the material. The provision of a screen should aim at causing the maximum overall loss to a radiated field, and the material chosen depends on whether the field is largely electric or magnetic.

In general, magnetic materials provide greater absorption loss to radiated electromagnetic energy, while good conductors, such as copper or aluminium, give more reflection loss. These latter materials make effective screens for electric fields, but their efficiency falls as frequency is increased. Aluminium is nevertheless commonly used for v.h.f. intermediate frequency transformer screening cans. In the presence of an alternating magnetic field, the screening efficiency of aluminium and copper falls as frequency decreases. At low (audio) frequencies, therefore, it is necessary to employ such high permeability metals as Mu-metal or Permalloy to provide satisfactory screening of magnetic fields.

Screening of cables

This is mainly influenced by the impedance of the radiating source and the pick-up cable.

High-impedance radiators

These are conductors having large series impedance (greater than $1 \text{k}\Omega$), in which h.f. voltages may be developed, with respect to earth, with very little current flowing. The radiation field is largely electric and can induce large h.f. voltages in adjacent high-impedance circuits, but little current in low-impedance circuits. A high-impedance circuit is here intended to mean a circuit having a high-termination impedance. A lead connected to the gate of a FET may therefore be considered to be a high-impedance circuit, and thus susceptible to such radiation. The use of copper-braid screening is effective in pick-up from such a source, provided that the screen is at earth potential along its entire length. For short leads earthing at one end is usually sufficient, but at high frequencies and for long leads the screening should normally be earthed at more than one point.

Low-impedance radiators

These are metallic conductors making a closed loop, which permits large currents to flow while developing little voltage. The fields resulting from such a source are largely magnetic and can induce large currents in low-impedance circuits but little voltage in high-impedance circuits. Conventional copper braiding is not effective in preventing magnetic coupling below 5 kHz but its effectiveness improves as frequency increases.

Earths and earth loops

Where, in a piece of electronic equipment, connections are made to earth at various points, currents may flow between such points, through the earth path. If these currents are at high frequency, the earth loops so formed can act as low-impedance radiators as defined above. The resulting fields, which are largely magnetic, can induce currents in low-impedance circuits, physically close to earth, which are difficult to remove. For this reason, in high-frequency equipment it is good practice to make earth connections at a single point.

The need for care in the use of multiple earths is not restricted to equipment operating at high frequencies. It is, for instance, of extreme importance in zero frequency (d.c.) amplifiers, in which requirements often couple high gain with low noise. In order to meet the low noise requirements, three different earths are commonly specified, signal earth, chassis earth and power earth. The first of these provides a reference for voltages and must therefore be kept "clean". Where it is necessary to make connection between the signal path and earth, for instance through a series $C-R$ network for stabilization purposes, it is to signal earth that such connection is made. It is necessary that the chassis of an amplifier be held at earth potential for safety in handling, and also so that screening cans, which are connected to the chassis, shall be effective as screens. A separate lead is therefore provided for earthing the chassis, and this too should be kept relatively free from noise. Since most noise arises from the power supplies, either in the form of ripple or in mains hum, the return path of power supplies is via a separate power earth connection. The three earths thus specified should not be "commoned" at the amplifier, but should be connected by separate leads to a single earth point at the power-supply unit. This ensures that noise currents do not flow in the signal and chassis earths, giving rise to noise voltages at the amplifier output.

APPENDIX C

Symbols used in this Book

British Standard Specification No. 3363, 1961, entitled "Letter symbols for light-current semi-conductor devices", makes recommendations for symbols to be used when describing transistor circuits. This system has been extended, in the same form, for use with FET and thermionic valve circuits and is stated briefly below.

Symbols

c or C,	Collector	
b or B,	Base	Bipolar transistor
e or E,	Emitter	
d or D,	Drain	
g or G,	Gate	Field effect transistor
s or S,	Source	
a or A,	Anode	
s or S,	Screen	
g or G,	Grid	Thermionic valve
k or K,	Cathode	
v or V,	Voltage	
i or I,	Current	
P,	Power	

$\left.\begin{matrix} i \\ v \end{matrix}\right\}$ with subscripts $\left\{\begin{matrix} c \\ b \\ e \end{matrix}\right\}$ or $\left\{\begin{matrix} d \\ g \\ s \end{matrix}\right\}$ represents the instantaneous value of a varying component.

$\left.\begin{matrix} i \\ v \end{matrix}\right\}$ with subscripts $\left\{\begin{matrix} C & D \\ B & \text{or} & G \\ E & S \end{matrix}\right\}$ represents the instantaneous total value.

$\left.\begin{matrix} I \\ V \end{matrix}\right\}$ with subscripts $\left\{\begin{matrix} c & d \\ b & \text{or} & g \\ e & s \end{matrix}\right\}$ represents the r.m.s. value of a varying component.

$\left.\begin{matrix} I \\ V \end{matrix}\right\}$ with subscripts $\left\{\begin{matrix} C & D \\ B & \text{or} & G \\ E & S \end{matrix}\right\}$ represents the d.c. or no-signal value.

Maximum and minimum values are indicated by the use of subscripts (max) and (min).

Electrical parameters

	Device	Associated circuit	Basic units
Resistance	r	R	
Reactance	x	X	Ω Ohms
Impedance	z	Z	
Admittance	y	Y	
Conductance	g	G	S Siemens
Inductance	l	L	H Henrys
Capacitance	c	C	F Farads

Double subscripts

Where capital V has two capital subscripts, this represents a voltage supply provided for the particular electrode of the device. For example, V_{CC} refers to a transistor collector supply voltage, and V_{DD} represents a voltage supply provided specifically for the drain of a FET. Where the two subscripts are different, the first subscript denotes the terminal at which the voltage is measured and the second subscript denotes the reference terminal. For example, V_{BE} represents the d.c. or no-signal voltage measured at the base, with respect to the emitter of a bipolar transistor. Other parameters may also be denoted by the use of double subscripts, as with c_{gs} the capacitance which exists between the gate and source of a FET, or $r_{bb'}$ the resistance between the actual base point and the base connector.

Matrix notation

The first subscript in the matrix notation for semiconductor devices identifies the element of the four-pole matrix. Thus,

i input
o output
f forward
r reverse

A second subscript is used to identify the circuit configuration:

e common emitter s common source
b common base g common gate
c common collector d common drain

For example, using h parameters for bipolar transistors,

$h_{ib}(h_{11})$ The small signal value of input impedance with the output short circuited to alternating current.

$h_{rb}(h_{12})$ The small signal value of reverse voltage transfer ratio with the output voltage held constant.

$h_{fb}(h_{21}, \alpha)$ }
$h_{fe}(h'_{21}, \beta)$ } The small signal forward current transfer ratio with the output short circuited to alternating current.

$h_{ob}(h_{22})$ }
$h_{oe}(h'_{22})$ } The small signal value of the output admittance with the input open circuited to alternating current.

Static values of parameters are indicated by capital subscripts, e.g.

h_{FE} The static value of the forward current transfer ratio, with the output voltage held constant.

Similarly, using y parameters for field effect transistors,

$y_{fs}(y_{21}, g_m)$ The small signal forward transfer conductance with the output voltage held at zero.

$y_{os}(y_{22}, 1/r_d)$ The small signal value of output conductance with the input voltage held at zero.

Additional symbols

$\left.\begin{array}{l} f_\alpha \\ f_\beta \end{array}\right\}$ The frequency at which the magnitude of the parameter indicated by the subscript is 0.707 of the low-frequency value.

f_1 The frequency at which the modulus of h_{fe} equals unity.

I_H Holding current for an SCR.

$\left.\begin{array}{l} I_{CBO} \\ I_{CEO} \end{array}\right\}$ Collector current when the collector is biased in the reverse direction with respect to the reference terminal and the other terminal is short circuited.

V_{BO} Break over voltage of an SCR.

V_{BR} Breakdown voltage.

$\left.\begin{array}{l} V_{(BR)CBO} \\ V_{(BR)CEO} \end{array}\right\}$ The breakdown voltage between the terminal indicated by the first subscript when it is biased in the reverse direction with respect to the reference terminal and the other terminal is short circuited.

$V_{CE(sat)}$ Collector-to-emitter saturation voltage.

$V_{CE(knee)}$ Collector knee voltage.

P_{tot} Total power dissipated within a device.

T_{amb} Ambient temperature.

T_j Junction temperature.

$\left.\begin{array}{l} r_{bb}, r_{be}, r_{bc} \\ r_{ce}, C_{be}, C_{bc} \\ C_{ce}, g_m \end{array}\right\}$ Components of the small signal hybrid-equivalent circuit.

g_m is also used as the mutual conductance of a thermionic valve.

r_a the anode resistance of a thermionic valve.

μ the amplification factor of a valve.

r_d the drain resistance of a FET, $(= 1/y_{os})$.

r_g the gate resistance of a FET, $(= 1/y_{is})$.

APPENDIX D

The Thermionic Valve

INTRODUCTION

A thermionic valve is a device which utilizes the flow of electrons through a vacuum or near vacuum. Electrons are emitted by a heated cathode and collected by an anode which is generally held at a positive voltage with respect to the cathode. The introduction of other electrodes enables the stream of electrons from cathode to anode to be suitably controlled. The whole electrode assembly is usually mounted in a glass envelope from which all gas has been evacuated, although in some types, a trace of gas is intentionally introduced to modify the valve characteristics.[63]

FUNCTIONAL SURVEY OF VALVE TYPES

D.1. The diode

The diode is the simplest form of thermionic valve comprising a heated emitting cathode and a collector anode. It has largely been superseded by the semiconductor diode which, in its various forms, has low forward resistance, better performance at h.f., no heater requirement, and a true zero.

The characteristic curve of a typical thermionic diode has the form shown in Fig. D.1b. Anode current I_A is plotted against anode voltage V_A, and an increase in heater voltage is seen to raise the value of I_A at which saturation occurs. Because electrons leave the cathode with a finite velocity, some anode current flows when $V_A = 0$. This current increases with cathode temperature giving a displacement of the characteristic to the left, of approximately 0.1 V per 10 per cent change in heater voltage.

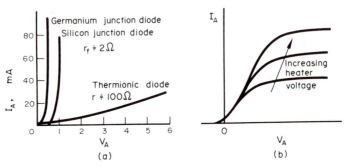

Fig. D.1. (a) Comparison of thermionic and semiconductor diodes. (b) Effect of heater voltages on diode characteristics.

Below saturation, the Three-halves Power Law[64] holds, i.e.

$$I_A = kV_A^{3/2}, \tag{D.1}$$

where k is a constant determined by the geometry of the valve.

D.2. The triode

A triode valve has three electrodes, a control grid being introduced between cathode and anode. The anode current is controlled by varying V_{GK}, the voltage between the grid and cathode. Small changes in V_{GK} can cause large changes in I_A with negligible expenditure of power in the grid circuit.

A typical family of anode characteristic curves is given in Fig. D.2 in which I_A is plotted against V_A with V_{GK} as parameter.

Using these curves, fundamental relationships may be defined.

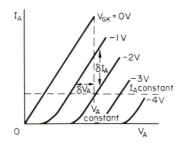

Fig. D.2. Typical anode characteristics of a triode.

(1) *Differential anode resistance*
The gradient of a curve at any point is

$$\left[\frac{\delta I_A}{\delta V_A}\right] (V_G \text{ constant}) \underset{\text{def}}{=} g_a = \frac{1}{r_a}, \qquad (D.2)$$

where r_a is the differential anode resistance.

(2) *Mutual conductance*
Intercepts of lines parallel to the current axis give

$$\left[\frac{\delta I_A}{\delta V_G}\right] (V_A \text{ constant}) \underset{\text{def}}{=} g_m, \qquad (D.3)$$

where g_m is the mutual conductance or transconductance.

(3) *Amplification factor*
Intercepts of lines parallel to the voltage axis give

$$\left[\frac{\delta V_A}{\delta V_G}\right] (I_A \text{ constant}) \underset{\text{def}}{=} \mu, \qquad (D.4)$$

where μ is the amplification factor.

Expression (D.1), giving the anode current of a diode as a function of anode voltage, can be extended for the triode

$$I_A = K \left(V_G + \frac{V_A}{\mu} \right)^{3/2}. \qquad (D.5)$$

Thus if V_G is negative and $V_G = - V_A/\mu$, then $I_A = 0$. This value of grid voltage is the *grid cut-off voltage* $V_{Gc/0}$, and is a function of μ and anode voltage.

Example
With an anode voltage of 180 V, a valve having $\mu = 50$ has a grid cut-off voltage,

$$V_{Gc/0} = - V_A / \mu = - 180/50 = - 3.6 \text{ V},$$

Since the cut-off voltage is inversely proportional to μ, high μ valves have a smaller input-handling capacity than low μ types for a given V_A. Usual operation is with the grid voltage in the range 0 V to $V_{Gc/0}$. If the grid is positive with respect to the cathode, it will attract electrons and grid current will flow. Under these conditions there is a low resistance between grid and cathode, of the order of 1000 Ω.

There are three general types of triode valves, typified by the 12AU7, 12AX7 and 12AT7, whose anode characteristics are given in Fig. D.3.

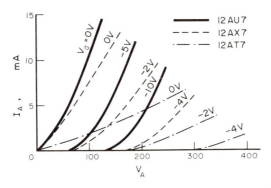

Fig. D.3. Anode characteristics of 12AT7, 12AU7 and 12AX7 triodes.

(a) Low μ, low g_m: 12AU7 with $\mu = 20$ and $g_m = 2$ mA/V.
(b) High μ, low g_m: 12AX7 with $\mu = 100$ and $g_m = 2$ mA/V.
(c) Medium μ, high g_m: 12AT7 with $\mu = 50$ and $g_m = 4$ mA/V.

Suggested uses for these three groups are:

(a) *Low μ.*   Where large input signals are to be handled, such as in frequency-multiplying tuned-amplifier stages.
(b) *High g_m.*   Cathode follower stage where the output resistance tends to $1/g_m$.
(c) *High μ.*   A voltage amplifier where the highest possible gain is required. For any common cathode amplifier the maximum gain is μ.

The group of valves having high g_m and medium μ is probably the more generally applicable type.

Applications
Amplifiers at low frequencies where interelectrode capacitance has only limited effect.

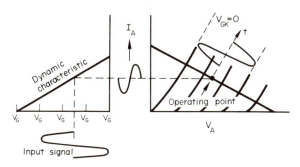

Fig. D.4. The triode as a linear amplifier.

Tuned amplifiers at v.h.f. where the low noise performance of a triode makes it preferable to a pentode.[65]

Oscillators of both sinusoidal and relaxation types. In many cases two triodes are mounted in the same envelope. This is very convenient for pulse networks of the multivibrator type.

D.3.   The tetrode (Fig. D.5)

The screen grid was introduced to enable h.f. amplification to be accomplished without the necessity of neutralizing the grid to anode capacitance (§ D.5). However, secondary emission effects,[64] when the anode is at a lower voltage than the screen grid, reduce the usefulness of the valve. This limitation led to the introduction of the suppressor grid in the pentode.

Beam tetrodes, in which the electron stream is directed in such a manner as to give a potential minimum between the screen grid and anode, were widely used for low- and medium-power amplifiers. The

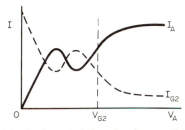

Fig. D.5. Elementary tetrode characteristics, showing negative resistance region due to secondary emission.

screen current in these types is a very small part of the cathode current as the grids are aligned and the screen grid intercepts few electrons.

Since the screen current performs no useful work, in most cases it is desirable that it should be as small as possible.

Applications

In addition to their use as power amplifiers, tetrodes were also widely used as series regulator valves in stabilized power supplies.

D.4.   The pentode

The suppressor grid produces a potential minimum between the anode and screen grid which prevents secondary electrons, generated at the anode, from being collected by the screen grid. The suppressor is usually maintained at the cathode voltage, but it can be used as a control grid with respect to anode current. Generally, $V_{Gc/0}$ is of the order of -50 V, but special purpose pentodes have been developed with suppressor cut-off of only a few volts.

Examination of the typical pentode characteristics of Fig. D.6 shows that beyond $V_A = 100$ V the curves are nearly parallel to the voltage axis, indicating a large r_a ($\doteqdot 1$ MΩ). Thus, above the knee of

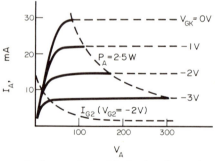

Fig. D.6. Typical pentode characteristics. The broken-line region of the curves shows where the maximum permissible anode dissipation is exceeded.

the curves the anode current is largely independent of anode voltage. This is because the screen grid voltage controls the anode current by providing the accelerating electric field. Due to the passive nature of the anode, the μ for pentodes is extremely high, commonly being greater than 1000.

At low values of V_A the curves run together. Thus, for a given load line the value of the minimum anode voltage is fixed. (This is not so for the triode.) The minimum anode voltage for a pentode is known as the bottoming voltage and is of importance in many "non-linear" operations. It should be noted that if V_{G2} is fixed, the cathode current $I_A + I_S$ is constant for a given value of V_{G1}.

Applications

Pentodes were widely used as tuned amplifiers because, due to small anode–grid capacitance, stable operation could be achieved without neutralization. Much larger gain–bandwidth products were obtained with pentodes than with triodes, because of their low effective input capacitance. They were also used as voltage amplifiers for low-frequency operation where large anode resistors could be used and the inherent high μ of the valves utilized. Very high gain could be obtained with low screen voltage giving the so-called "starvation condition". The circuit of Fig. D.7 illustrates how the pentode may be used for gating purposes if the suppressor is used as a control grid.

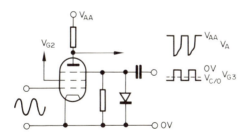

Fig. D.7. Use of a pentode for gating purposes. The gating waveform is applied to the suppressor grid.

D.5. Grid input admittance

The interelectrode capacitances of a triode may be shown as in Fig. D.8 in which C_{ag} is the anode–grid capacitance and C_{gk} the capacitance which exists between grid and cathode,

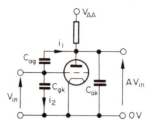

Fig. D.8. Interelectrode capacitances of a triode.

Input admittance $= i_{in}/v_{in} = (i_1 + i_2)/v_{in}$, where

$$i_{in} = v_{in}(1 - A)sC_{ag} \quad \text{and} \quad i_2 = v_{in}sC_{gk}.$$

Therefore,

$$\text{Input admittance} = s(C_{gk} + (1 - A)C_{ag}). \qquad \text{(D.6)}$$

The symbol s is the Laplace variable and where consideration is limited to sinusoidal operation this may be replaced by $j\omega$.

Hence,

$$\text{Input admittance} = j\omega[C_{gk} + (1 - A)C_{ag}]. \qquad \text{(D.7)}$$

The input capacitance is thus increased from C_{gk} to

$$C_{gk} + (1 - A)C_{ag},$$

where A is negative and greater than 1 at medium frequencies. This increase in effective input capacitance, due to the presence of anode–grid capacitance is the *Miller effect*,[66] and it was to reduce this effect that the screen grid was incorporated in the thermionic valve.

D.6. Auxiliary voltage supplies

Cathode bias

It is common practice to derive the auxiliary voltage supplies from the positive voltage rail which provides the anode supply. For a triode, a grid–cathode bias voltage is normally required to maintain the correct operating point, and cathode bias is used. This has two forms whose use depends on whether the amplifier is capacitor coupled or of the zero-frequency type.

The cathode resistor R_K, in Fig. D.9, in addition to providing the bias voltage, by negative current feedback, stabilizes the working point against variations such as ageing of the valve.

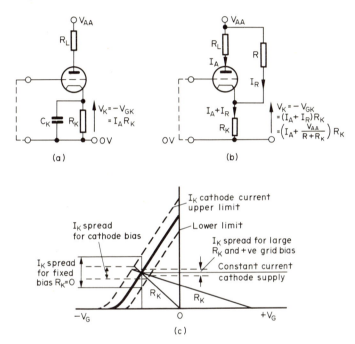

Fig. D.9. Provision of cathode bias. The possible variation of operating point for cathode bias is less than for fixed grid bias, but is greater than for an ideal constant current supply. This latter can be approached by returning the grid to a positive supply.

To eliminate the negative feedback at signal frequencies and the consequent loss in gain, R_K is bypassed by a capacitor of such value that in the required frequency range its reactance is negligible (see § 4.1).

If the loss in gain at zero frequency cannot be tolerated, the circuit of Fig. D.9b may be used. Negative feedback is greatly reduced by making R_K as small as possible, and the correct bias obtained by the steady current drawn through R. A typical value for I_R is $10I_A$.

Then,

$$I_R = V_{AA}/(R + R_K) \doteqdot V_{AA}/R.$$

Also,

$$R_K = V_{GK}/(I_A + I_R) \doteq V_{GK}/I_R.$$

Therefore

$$V_K = -V_{GK} = (I_A + I_R)R_K = [I_A + V_{AA}/(R + R_K)]R_K.$$

D.7.   Screen grid supply

There are two commonly used methods of obtaining the screen grid supply from the positive voltage rail, (1) current and (2) voltage, as shown in Fig. D.10a and b.

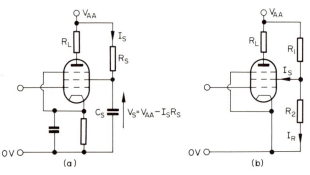

Fig. D.10. Provision of screen grid supply from positive voltage rail, (a) current, (b) voltage.

Screen current supply

If V_S is the required screen voltage, the current at that voltage is determined either from the valve characteristic curves or experimentally. Then $R_S = (V_{AA} - V_S)/I_S$. To eliminate gain reduction the screen must be decoupled by the capacitor C_S. Negative feedback makes this method unsuitable for use in zero frequency amplifiers.

Screen voltage supply

The voltage V_S is kept relatively constant by making I_R much greater than I_S, typically $I_R = 10I_S$. Then $R_2 = V_S/I_R$, and $R_1 = (V_{AA} - V_S)/(I_R + I_S)$. The disadvantage of this method is the drain on the h.t. power supply.

D.8.   Elementary valve equivalent networks

For input signals of small amplitudes the valve parameters g_m, μ and r_a can be considered as constants whose values are those measured at the operating point. Figure D.11 shows how these parameters vary with I_A.

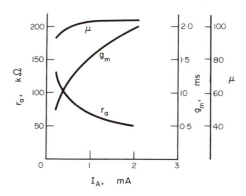

Fig. D.11. Variation of g_m, μ and r_a, with I_A as parameter, for an ECC85.

The anode current is a function of both grid voltage and anode voltage:

$$I_A = \frac{\delta I_A}{\delta V_G}\Delta V_G + \frac{\delta I_A}{\delta V_A}\Delta V_A. \qquad \text{(D.8)}$$

If, for convenience, ΔI_A is written as i_a, an incremental change in anode current about the standing value I_A, and if ΔV_A is similarly represented as v_a, then

$$i_a = g_m v_g + g_a v_a. \qquad \text{(D.9)}$$

This may be represented diagrammatically in the forms of Fig. D.12.

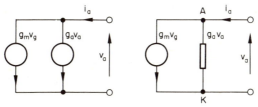

Fig. D.12. Diagrammatic representation of eqn. (D.9) using current generators.

Introducing an anode load resistor, R_L as in Fig. D.13a, the equivalent network may be further developed as in Fig. D.13b.

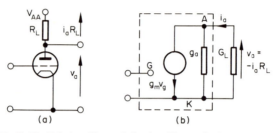

(a)   (b)

Fig. D.13. Triode with anode load and its equivalent network.

As the anode voltage v_a is a function of anode current, i.e. $v_a = -i_a R_L$, eqn. (D.9) may be written thus:

$$i_a = g_m v_g - i_a R_L / r_a.$$

Therefore

$$i_a r_a = g_m v_g r_a - i_a R_L.$$

But,

$$\mu = g_m \cdot r_a, \tag{D.10}$$

therefore

$$i_a = \frac{\mu v_g}{r_a + R_L}.$$

This expression provides the alternative equivalent network of Fig. D.14.

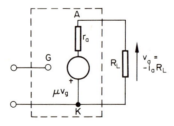

Fig. D.14. Alternative equivalent network of the circuit of Fig. D.13, using a voltage generator.

The voltage gain of the circuit may be written in the two forms as represented in the two equivalent networks. Thus:

$$v_a/v_g = -g_m/(g_a + G_L) = -g_mR,\qquad \text{(D.11a)}$$

where

$$R = 1/(g_a + G_L),$$

and

$$\frac{v_a}{v_g} = \frac{-\mu R_L}{r_a + R_L}.\qquad \text{(D.11b)}$$

A valve used in this way is said to be in *common cathode operation*.

D.9. Resistance in the cathode

The circuit equations of Fig. D.15 are

$$i_a = \frac{\mu v_{gk}}{r_a + R_L + R_K}\quad \text{and}\quad v_{gk} = v_{in} - i_a R_K.$$

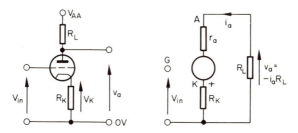

Fig. D.15. Effect of cathode resistor.

Therefore

$$i_a = \frac{\mu v_{in}}{r_a + R_L + (\mu + 1)R_K} = \frac{\mu v_{in}}{r'_a + R_L},\qquad \text{(D.12)}$$

where

$$r'_a = r_a + (\mu + 1)R_K.$$

The effective value of anode resistance is thus increased by the term $(\mu + 1)R_K$, and the equivalent network redrawn as in Fig. D.16.

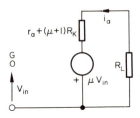

Fig. D.16. Alternative equivalent network of the circuit of Fig. D.15. R_K is multiplied by $(\mu + 1)$ and transferred to the anode circuit.

Example

Given a valve having an anode resistance $r_a = 10\,\text{k}\Omega$ and gain $\mu = 50$, let $R_K = 1\,\text{k}\Omega$, and $R_L = 10\,\text{k}\Omega$. $r'_a = r_a + (\mu + 1)R_K = 10\,\text{k}\Omega + 51\,\text{k}\Omega = 61\,\text{k}\Omega$.

In the absence of a cathode resistor, the voltage gain would be

$$A_v = -\mu R_L / (r_a + R_L) = -25.$$

This is modified by the cathode resistor thus:

$$A_v = -\mu R_L / (r'_a + R_L) = -7.$$

In the presence of both anode and cathode resistors, cathode voltage

$$v_k = i_a R_K = \frac{\mu R_K}{r_a + R_L + (\mu + 1)R_K} v_{in}, \qquad (D.13)$$

$$\frac{\mu R_K / (\mu + 1)}{[(r_a + R_L)/(\mu + 1)] + R_K} v_{in} = \frac{\mu'' R_K}{r''_a + R_K} v_{in}, \qquad (D.14)$$

where

$$\mu'' = \frac{\mu}{\mu + 1} \quad \text{and} \quad r''_a = \frac{r_a + R_L}{\mu + 1}.$$

Example

Using the same values as in the previous example,

$$\mu'' = 50/51 = 0.98, \qquad r''_a = 20\,\text{k}\Omega/51 = 390\,\Omega$$

and using expression (D.14)

$$\frac{v_k}{v_{in}} = \frac{0.98 \times 1\,\text{k}\Omega}{390 + 1\,\text{k}\Omega} = 0.7.$$

In the special case when $R_L = 0$, the valve is operated as a *cathode follower*.

Then,

$$\text{gain} = \frac{v_k}{v_{in}} = \frac{\mu R_K/(\mu + 1)}{[r_a/(\mu + 1)] + R_K} = 0.81. \tag{D.15}$$

The gain of a cathode follower tends to unity if R_K is much greater than $r_a/(\mu + 1)$, and μ is much greater than 1.

The output resistance of a cathode follower tends to $1/g_m$ if μ is much greater than 1.

The cathode follower may be used as an impedance converter providing low output impedance from a high impedance source.

D.10.   Signal injected at cathode

The circuit of Fig. D.17 is that of a common or "grounded" grid amplifier:

$$i_a = \frac{\mu v_{gk} - v_{in}}{r_a + R_L} \quad \text{and} \quad v_{gk} = v_{in}.$$

Therefore

$$i_a = \frac{-(\mu + 1)v_{in}}{r_a + R_L}, \tag{D.16}$$

and

$$v_a = \frac{(\mu + 1)v_{in}R_L}{r_a + R_L}. \tag{D.17}$$

This is similar to eqn. (D.11) except that μ has been replaced by $(\mu + 1)$. The main difference between common cathode and common

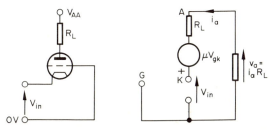

Fig. D.17. Grounded grid amplifier. The input resistance is $(r_a + R_L)/(\mu + 1)$ because the anode current flows through the input circuit. No signal inversion occurs.

grid operation is the resistance which the valve presents to the input signal source. In the common cathode case this is ideally infinite. The input resistance of a common grid amplifier, however, is

$$R_{in} = \frac{v_{in}}{i_a} \quad \text{(since the anode current flows through the input circuit)}$$

$$= v_{in} \times \frac{r_a + R_L}{(\mu + 1)v_{in}} = \frac{r_a + R_L}{(\mu + 1)}. \tag{D.18}$$

This normally has a value of a few hundred ohms, which means that the amplifier must be fed from a low-resistance source such as a cathode follower.

D.11.   Design from characteristics

The load line

For a given resistive load a line can be drawn on the anode characteristic giving the locus of points representing the anode voltage and current corresponding to the grid-to-cathode voltage. This line, the load line, has slope $-1/R_L$ (Fig. D.18).

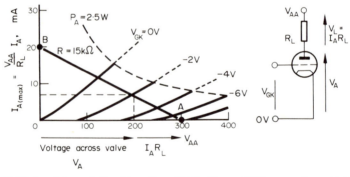

Fig. D.18. Load-line relationships, $R_L = 15\,\text{k}\Omega$, $V_{AA} = 300\,\text{V}$, operating grid bias = $-2\,\text{V}$.

Points A and B are the limits of the locus. When the valve is "cut-off" the anode current is zero and the anode voltage is the supply voltage, that is, point A on the characteristics ($V_A = V_{AA}$, $I_A = 0$). Point B is found by determining the current that would flow if the voltage across the valve was zero, that is $I_{A(\text{max})} = V_{AA}/R_L$.

The equation of the load line is thus:

$$I_A = -G_L V_A + I_{A(\text{max})}. \tag{D.19}$$

For normal linear operation a point on the load line is chosen as operating point so that equal excursions in grid voltage about that point give equal intervals on the load line, as shown in Fig. D.4.

Modification for cathode bias

In the presence of a cathode resistor some modification of Fig. D.18 is necessary. Let the cathode resistor be used to provide a bias of 2 V, then at standing anode current of $I_A = 6\,\text{mA}$,

$$V_{\text{in}} = V_{GK} + I_A R_K. \tag{D.20}$$

Using this expression Table D.1 can be constructed, and Fig. D.18 redrawn as in Fig. D.19.

Table D.1.

V_{GK}	$I_A\,(\text{mA})$	$V_K = I_A R_K$	$V_{\text{in}} = V_{GK} + I_A R_K$
0	11.4	3.5	3.5
−2	6.4	2.0	0
−4	3.0	0.93	−3.1
−6	0.9	0.28	−5.7

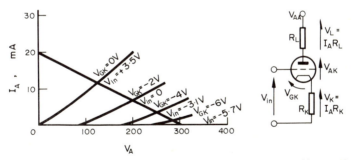

Fig. D.19. Effect of cathode bias resistor. Note the increased range of input voltage.

It is apparent that the gain has been reduced and that the voltage-handling capacity of the valve increased from 6 to 9 V. It is now also possible for the input voltage to go positive without the valve drawing grid current. In a.c. amplifiers the cathode resistor is normally bypassed with a large capacitor, and at the operating frequencies this effect of R_K is eliminated.

Valve with large cathode resistor

If R_K is large it is necessary to plot a load line having the value $R_L + R_K$, and, as previously, consider the circuit as having an input voltage $V_{in} = V_{GK} + I_A R_L$.

Example

The symmetrical cathode-coupled amplifier of Fig. D.20. The anode voltages can be determined by considering one valve. Since the anode currents of both valves pass through R_K, the cathode

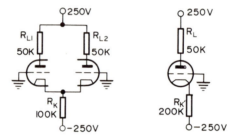

Fig. D.20. Symmetrical cathode coupled amplifier with an equivalent single-valve circuit for the balanced condition.

voltage is $V_K = 2I_A R_K = I_A \times 2R_K$, i.e. as if the anode current of one valve passes through a cathode resistor equal to $2R_K$. A load line must therefore be drawn having a value $R_L + 2R_K$ as in Fig. D.21.

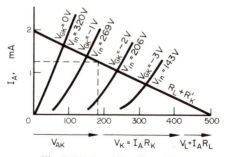

Fig. D.21. Load line $R_L = 2R_K$.

The approximate d.c. condition can be found in the following way. With the grids earthed the voltage between the negative rail and grid, $V_{in} = 250$ V. If the valves are to work in a linear manner the voltage dropped across R_K must be within a few volts of that between the negative rail and the grid, i.e. 250 V. The cathode current is thus determined by the value of the cathode resistor,

$$I_K = V_K/R_K = 250/100 \text{ k}\Omega = 2.5 \text{ mA}.$$

This current is shared between the two valves

$$I_{A1} = I_{A2} = 1.25 \text{ mA}$$

in the balanced condition.

$$V_{A1} = V_{A2} = V_{AA} - I_A R_L = 250 - (1.25 \times 50 \text{ k}\Omega) = 187.5 \text{ V}.$$

From the load line $V_{GK} = -1.3$ V.

This method of determining the approximate d.c. conditions can often be used with cathode-coupled circuits.

Cathode follower

In Fig. D.22 the load line for $R_K = 10 \text{ k}\Omega$ is set up on the characteristic curves.

$$V_{in} = V_{GK} + V_K = I_A R_K,$$

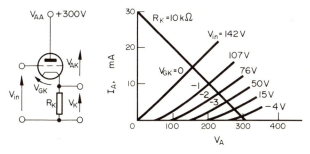

Fig. D.22. The cathode follower. A load line for $R_L = 10 \text{ k}\Omega$ is plotted on the characteristic curves, together with the equivalent input voltages.

where V_K is the output voltage V_{out}. From the load line the V_{out}/V_{in} curve of Fig. D.23 can be constructed.

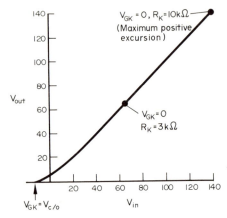

Fig. D.23. V_{out}/V_{in} curve for the cathode follower. Note that an increase in the value of R_K increases the signal-handling ability without changing the gain from unity.

When the input voltage $V_{in} = 0$ the output voltage equals $V_{out} = -V_{GK} = 6.5$ V from the load line. When the cathode resistor is reduced, the voltage that the cathode follower can use over its linear range is reduced, but the input/output voltage relationship is little changed. The output voltage is a linear function of the input voltage and largely independent of the output current.

Bibliography

1. Shockley, W., *Bell Syst. Tech. J.* **28**, July 1949.
2. *The Hot Carrier Diode*, Hewlett Packard Application Note 907.
3. Mazda, F. F., *The Components of Computers—Optical Devices*, Elect. Components, London, Feb. 1973.
4. Gooch, C. H., *Electroluminescent Diode Displays*, Elect. Components, London, June 1972.
5. *Microwave Applications of Semiconductors*, Proc. Joint I.E.R.E.–I.E.E. Symp., London, July 1965.
6. *Applications of PIN Diodes*, Hewlett Packard Application Note 922.
7. Day, D. B., *J. Brit. Inst. Radio Engrs*, **21**, 3, London, Mar. 1961.
8. Penfield, P. and Rafuse, R. P., *Varactor Diode*; *Varactor Applications*, M.I.T. Press, Cambridge, Mass., 1962.
9. *Harmonic Generation using Step Recovery Diodes*, Hewlett Packard Application Note 920.
10. Hosking, M. W., *The Realm of Microwaves*, Wireless World, London, Feb. 1973.
11. Carroll, J. F., *Impatt, Trapatt, Gunn and l.s.a. Devices*, Arnold, London, 1970.
12. Thompson, P. A. and Bateson, J., *J. Brit. Inst. Radio Engrs*, **22**, 1, London, July 1961.
13. Shockley, W., *Holes and Electrons in Semiconductors*, Van Nostrand, New York, 1950.
14. James, J. R. and Bradley, D. J., *Electron. Technol.* **38**, Mar. 1961.
15. Ebers, J. J. and Moll, J. L., *Proc. Inst. Radio Engrs*, **42**, New York, Dec. 1954.
16. Ryder-Smith, S. C., *Electron. Technol.* **38**, Oct. 1961.
17. Chandi, S. K., *Trans. Inst. Radio Engrs*, C.T. **4**, New York, Sept. 1957.
18. Shea, R. F., *Transistor Circuit Engineering*, Wiley, New York, 1958.
19. *Silicon Controlled Rectifiers*, A.E.I. Application Report 4450–205.
20. *Thyristors and Rectifiers*, R.C.A. Data book SSD-206.
21. Mazda, F. F., *Controlled Rectification*, Elect. Components, London, Jan. 1971.
22. *Heatsinks for Semiconductor Rectifiers and Thyristors*, S.T.C. Publication MF/187 X.
23. Bisson, D. K. and Dyer, R.F., *Trans. A.I.E.E. Comm. and Elect.*, May 1959.
24. *Transistor Manual*, General Electric Inc., 1964.
25. Crawford, R. H. and Dean, R. T., *The How and Why of Unijunction Transistors*, Texas Inst. Publication.
26. Watson, J., *An Introduction to Field Effect Transistors*, Siliconix Publication.
27. Sevin, L. J., *Field Effect Transistors*, Texas Inst. Publication, April 1963.
28. Sparkes, J. J., *The Radio and Elect. Engr.* **43**, London, Jan. 1973.
29. Brothers, J. S., *The Radio and Elect. Engr.* **43**, London, Jan. 1973.
30. Dean, K. J., *The Radio and Elect. Engr.* **43**, London, Jan. 1973.
31. Gosling, W., *The Radio and Elect. Engr.* **43**, London, Jan. 1973.
32. Boyle, W. S. and Smith, G. E., *Bell Syst. Tech. J.* **49**, 1970.

33. Beynon, J. D., *Electronics and Power*, I.E.E., London, May 1973.
34. Amelio, G. F., *The Impact of Large CCD Arrays*, Elect. Components, London, Feb. 1975.
35. *International Conference on the Technology and Applications of Charge-coupled Devices*, I.E.E., R.R.E., Edinburgh University, Sept. 1974.
36. Valley, G. E. and Wallman, H., *Vacuum Tube Amplifiers*, McGraw-Hill, New York, 1948.
37. Sturley, K. R., *Radio Receiver Design*, Chapman & Hall, London, 1947.
38. Langford-Smith, F., *Radio Designers Handbook*, Iliffe, London, 1953.
39. Joyce, M. V. and Clarke, K. K., *Transistor Circuit Analysis*, Addison-Wesley, New York, 1961.
40. Korne, G. A. and Korne, T. M., *Electronic Analog Computers*, McGraw-Hill, New York, 1952.
41. Paul, R. J., *Fundamental Analogue Techniques*, Blackie, London, 1964.
42. Hyndman, D. E., *Analog and Hybrid Computing*, Pergamon, Oxford, 1970.
43. Lynch, W. A., *Proc. Inst. Radio Engrs*, **39**, New York, Sept. 1951.
44. Benson, F. A., *Electron. Engng*, **24**, Sept. 1952.
45. Walker, D. E., *Electron. Engng*, **34**, June 1962.
46. Brunetti, C., *Proc. Inst. Radio Engrs*, **27**, New York, 1929.
47. Sommers, H. S., *Proc. Inst. Radio Engrs*, **47**, New York, 1959.
48. van der Pol, B., *Phil. Mag.* **2**, 1926.
49. Abraham, H. and Bloch, E., *Ann. der Physik*, **12**, 1919.
50. Millman, J. and Taub, H., *Pulse and Digital Circuits*, McGraw-Hill, New York, 1956.
51. Eccles, W. H. and Jordan, F. W., *Radio Rev.* **1**, London, 1919.
52. Chance, B., *Waveforms*, McGraw-Hill, New York, 1948.
53. Neeteson, P. A., *Junction Transistors in Pulse Circuits*, Philips Tech. Lib., Eindhoven, 1959.
54. Beaufoy, R., *J. Inst. Elect. Engrs*, May 1959.
55. Dummer, G. W., *Fixed Resistors*, Pitman, London, 1956.
56. Bardsley, M. and Dyson, A. F., *The Radio and Elect. Engr.*, **44**, 4, London, April 1974.
57. Dummer, G. W., *Fixed Capacitors*, Pitman, London, 1956.
58. *Electron. Prod. Mag.*, U.T.P. New York, Dec. 1968.
59. Pearlston, C. B., *Trans. Inst. Radio Engrs*, R.F. **14**, New York, Oct. 1962.
60. Jaeger, J. C., *An Introduction to the Laplace Transformation with Engineering Applications*, Methuen, London, 1949.
61. van Valkenburg, M. E., *Introduction to Modern Network Synthesis*, Wiley, New York, 1959.
62. Weinburg, I., *Network Analysis and Synthesis*, McGraw-Hill, New York, 1962.
63. Zimmerman, H. J. and Mason, S. J., *Electronic Circuitry Theory*, Wiley, New York, 1959.
64. Langmuir, I., *Phys. Rev.* **2**, 1913.
65. Valley, G. E. and Wallman, H., *Vacuum Tube Amplifiers*, McGraw-Hill, New York, 1948.
66. Miller, J. M., *Sci. Pap. U.S. Bur. Stand.*, No 351, 1919.

Index